FIELD GEOLOGY IN COLOUR

FIELD GEOLOGY
in colour

by J. F. KIRKALDY, D. Sc.
Emeritus Professor of Geology
formerly Head of the Department of Geology
Queen Mary College, London.

photographs by

FOLKE JOHANSSON

and

MICHAEL ALLMAN

NEW ORCHARD EDITIONS

New Orchard Editions Ltd
Stanley House
3 Fleets Lane
Poole, Dorset BH15 3AJ

First published in the English edition 1963

2nd impression November 1964
3rd impression December 1965
2nd edition January 1968
reprinted January 1970
reprinted January 1972
reprinted February 1973
3rd edition 1976
This edition published 1988

ISBN 1 85079 133 3

Printed and bound in Great Britain by
Richard Clay Ltd., Bungay, Suffolk

CONTENTS

PREFACE 8

I GEOLOGICAL FIELD WORK 11

1 THE EXAMINATION OF EXPOSURES 11

Localities for Field Work 11
Equipment for Field Work 12
The Geological Hammer 12
Labelling Specimens 14
Care and Safety During Field Work 15
A Code for Geological Field Work 15
'Reading' Exposures 16
Critical Exposures 16
The Field Notebook 17
Field Sketching 17
Field Identification 19
Compass and Clinometer 20
The Systematic Examination of Exposures 23
Planning Field Work 24
Between Exposures 25

2 GEOLOGICAL MAPPING 27

First steps 27
Hard and Dotted Boundaries 28
Recording One's Evidence 29
Soft-rock and Hard-rock Geology 31
Mapping on Soft-rocks 31
Tracing Features 32
Mapping Drift Deposits 34
Superficial Structures 36
Mapping Faults 38
Mapping on Hard-rocks 39
The Importance of Small Scale Structures 40
Folding and Cleavage or Foliation 41

Veins and Joints 44
Writing the Report 45

II ROCKS AND STRUCTURES TO BE OBSERVED IN THE FIELD 47

3 SEDIMENTARY ROCKS 47

Clastic Rocks 48
Rudaceous Rocks 48
Ill-graded Deposits of Glacial Origin 49
Residual Deposits 51
Arenaceous Rocks 51
Argillaceous Rocks 53
Pre-lithification Deformation 53
Turbidites 54
Chemical Deposits 55
Organic Deposits 57
Limestones and other Carbonates 59
Chemical Structures of Secondary Origin 61
Fossils in Field Work 61
Breaks in Deposition and Unconformities 64

4 GEOLOGICAL STRUCTURES 66

Folds 66
Faults 70
Jointing 72
Veining 73

5 IGNEOUS ROCKS 74

Extrusive Rocks 74
Pyroclastic Rocks 76
Intrusive Rocks 76
Igneous Relationships 80

COLOUR PLATES 81

6 METAMORPHIC ROCKS AND STRUCTURES 145

Thermal Metamorphism 145
Dynamic Metamorphism 145

Regional Metamorphism 145

7 THE WEATHERING OF ROCKS 147

III COLOUR PLATE DESCRIPTIONS 149

IV LOCALITIES FOR FIELD WORK 205

8 SOURCES OF INFORMATION 205

Publications of the Institute of Geological Sciences 205
Publications of Geological Societies and other Bodies 206

9 SUPPLIERS OF FIELD EQUIPMENT 208

10 PHOTOGRAPHY IN THE FIELD 209

INDEX 211

PREFACE

Geology, the study of the form, nature and history of the Earth, is one of the 'field' sciences. With the recent development of highly sophisticated equipment, it is possible to investigate in very great detail, the chemical and physical properties of the materials – rocks and minerals – that form the crust of the Earth. It is possible to determine the time, measurable in millions of years, that has elapsed since they were formed. But if all this elaborate laboratory investigation is to be worthwhile, it is essential that the 'field relationships' of the rocks and minerals be known.

The first specimens from the surface of the Moon were grabbed up by a robot. They were then subjected to extremely comprehensive laboratory investigations, but whilst these produced a vast amount of information, there were still many uncertainties. It was realized that to obtain the maximum return for the vast expense of Lunar research, it was necessary to train a geologist in space flight, so that he could be landed on the Moon to select the specimens for further investigation, to record their field relationships and to study, at first hand, the features of the Lunar landscape.

Field work, supplemented by laboratory studies, has been the foundation for our present knowledge of the geology of the Earth. The latest exciting concepts of Plate Tectonics and Continental Shifting, well publicized by many good television programmes and books, have developed from the synthesis of field work on the continents with the technological developments that have made possible drilling in deep water (and hence the sampling of the rocks that underlie the ocean floors), the laboratory techniques for dating rocks whether from the continents or from the ocean floors and for determining their position at a particular moment of the geological past relative to the Earth's magnetic pole.

This book has been planned to give guidance on the field work that can be done with a minimum of equipment – hammer, handlens, notebook and pencil, map and compass/clinometer. To these must be added an eye trained to recognize and appreciate the significance of changes, often subtle changes, in landscape, in the disposition of the beds and in the detail visible on the exposed surface of rock. The features shown in the colour plates and described in the relevant text range from the clearly obvious to those which can only be detected by careful observation. The colour plates have been selected from many different localities to cover as wide a range of rock types and field occurrences as possible.

The reader is referred to Professor Kirkaldy's two companion books in this series, *Minerals and Rocks in Colour* and *Fossils in Colour* for a fuller treatment, including the identification, of the commoner minerals, rocks and fossils, than is possible in this text.

It is assumed that the reader is familiar with the geologist's time-scale – the Stratigraphical Table – as set out below, and also familiar with the principles on which it is based.

The Stratigraphical Table

ERA	PERIOD	DURATION IN MILLIONS OF YEARS	BEGINNING OF PERIOD FROM PRESENT IN MILLIONS OF YEARS
Quaternary	Holocene		0.01
	Pleistocene	circa 2	circa 2
Tertiary	Pliocene	5	7
	Miocene	19	26
	Oligocene	12	38
	Eocene	27	65
Mesozoic	Cretaceous	70	135
	Jurassic	60	195
	Triassic	30	225
Palaeozoic	Permian	55	280
	Carboniferous	65	345
	Devonian	50	395
	Silurian	35	430
	Ordovician	70	500
	Cambrian	70	570
Pre-Cambrian or Pre-Phanerozoic			4600

Also that during the geological past, there have been periods of great crustal disturbance, orogenic episodes, when the rocks of belts of the Earth's crust have been folded and contorted, altered (metamorphosed) into new rock-types and intruded from below by great masses of rock at high temperature. The geographical conditions at any one locality have also changed greatly. At one time it may have been submerged by the sea, at another it was a land area, perhaps covered by ice sheets or subjected to desert-like conditions.

It is on the careful field work of geologists during the past two centuries that our present knowledge of the enthralling and complicated story of the Earth's geological history is based. Much still remains to be deciphered.

D. E. B. Bates
J. F. Kirkaldy
April 1976

Geology Department
University College of Wales
Aberystwyth
Dyfed, Wales

Stone House
Byfield Road
Chipping Warden
Near Banbury
Oxfordshire

ACKNOWLEDGEMENTS

The authors would like to thank the following colleagues for the loan of transparencies for reproduction in the colour section: Dr. D. Q. Bowen (Nos 13, 14, 16, 17); Mr. H. J. E. Convery (No. 40); Dr. J. Dennison (No. 31); Dr. W. R. Fitches (Nos 143, 146); Dr. G. P. Larwood (Nos 51, 55); Dr. J. R. Haynes (No. 103); Dr. A. S. G. Jones (Nos 3, 148); Dr. A. J. Maltman (Nos 19, 110, 112, 113, 123, 124, 144, 149); Dr. W. J. Phillips (Nos 131, 133, 137, 140); Dr. R. C. Whatley (No. 15); Professor A. Wood (No. 71); Mr. A. Wyatt (No. 30).

I GEOLOGICAL FIELD WORK

1 THE EXAMINATION OF EXPOSURES

Field work to a geologist is much more than the casual collecting of curious looking objects, often fossils, or of attractive looking minerals or rocks. Such casual collecting may often develop into a closer examination of the different kinds of rocks that can be seen, perhaps in the cliffs behind a bay. Are the rocks lying just haphazard or are they arranged in some orderly manner? Are fossils to be found only in certain beds and are there any changes in the fossil content of the different layers? If minerals are present, are they too restricted in their occurrence and if so, in what way? Then in the next bay, somewhat different rocks may be seen. What is the reason for this? The casual collector is now developing into a field geologist, for he has begun to study the different types of rocks, their nature and also their relationships. He will soon feel the need to record (write down or sketch) his observations in an orderly way and also he may mark on his map the places where certain distinctive rocks cut the surface of the ground. He is beginning to make a geological map showing the outcrop of this bed. If he examines the rocks closely he will note features, perhaps puzzling features, that may provide clues as to the conditions under which a particular rock was formed and of the changes which that rock has undergone since its formation.

Geological field work is exciting, for one is always trying to 'read' the rocks and to unravel clues that will reveal their history. There is always the possibility of making some new discovery, but the value of such a discovery will be greatly diminished if the relationships of the relevant rocks have not been properly observed and recorded. So field work should always be carried out in a planned and systematic manner.

Localities for Field Work

Areas containing a wide variety of interesting rocks and with plenty of exposures, either natural (cliffs, stream sections, etc.) or man-made (quarries, road and other cuttings, etc.) are, at first sight, the obvious places to visit. But field work can be carried out anywhere, even in the built-up cities and towns, though here one is very dependent on the temporary exposures provided by building operations, by the trenches opened for cable laying, etc. In poorly exposed ground or where the rocks are rather monotonous in character, one may have to work the more diligently to obtain significant evidence.

The most spectacular exposures are to be found in coastal or in mountainous areas. A wave-cut platform is very useful, for on its nearly horizontal surface such features as fold and fault patterns can be seen in plan (see No. 76)*, whilst these may also be visible in section in the cliffs behind, so that the three-dimensional picture can be readily appreciated. In mountain areas it is the vertical relief which is often spectacular and instructive in unravelling the structure of the rocks, and this is aided by extensive areas of outcrop (e.g. No. 6). Water action in streams or on the shore, by smoothing the rock surface (often with a finely frosted 'matt' texture which is better examined when wet) is invaluable in revealing the more detailed textures (see No. 136).

In more gentle terrain, particularly inland, superficial (drift) deposits may conceal the solid rocks extensively. Natural exposures have to be sought on hill tops and sides, and in stream beds. Artificial exposures are correspondingly more important. Quarries and road and railway cuttings are good locations (right of access and safety are important matters in these cases). They can provide long continuous sections, with often a three-dimensional picture in the quarries. Outcrops in lanes and roads, worn down by traffic, were formerly numerous, but tarring has obscured many of these, whilst the banks may be mantled with downwash or heavily overgrown. At a more humble level, ditches and temporary excavations provide useful exposures. Temporary exposures that have uncovered interesting features, such as a richly fossiliferous layer that had not been seen for many years previously or a detailed section in drift deposits or showing an igneous dyke unexposed for many miles along its length, have formed the subject of numerous communications, often written by non-professional geologists, to the journals of geological societies.

*Throughout the text, colour plates are referred to as No. 1, Nos 3 and 4, etc. and line illustrations within the text are referred to as Fig. 1, etc.

Equipment for Field Work

First, waterproof clothing and strong footwear are essential for working in all weathers in rough and often distinctly muddy country, together with a rucksack or haversack for carrying not only the day's sustenance, but also the tools that a geologist needs. These tools are hammer, chisel and packing material for specimens, plus a notebook, map and pencils for recording observations, together with a handlens and probably a camera; for detailed work a compass/clinometer (see Chapter 9) is also needed. It is worth taking trouble in choosing one's equipment, making sure that it feels right and learning to use it to the best advantage.

The Geological Hammer

A geological hammer is a carefully designed tool made of specially hardened steel. It cannot be bought from the normal ironmonger. The hammers which they supply for domestic and a number of trade purposes are made of steel too soft to be used safely on rocks. Such hammers splinter easily and the flying slivers can cause nasty wounds, particularly to the eyes, not only of the hammerer but also of his companions. The head of a geological hammer must be firmly attached to the shaft. Hammers with the head and shaft cast in one piece are certainly very strong, but they are short and do not have the well-balanced feel of a wooden shaft of the right length. They are also distinctly expensive. If the wood of the shaft shrinks, loosening the head, this can usually be quickly put right by soaking the hammer head in a rock pool or in a stream. In dry climates, however, shrinkage can become such a problem that a steel-shafted hammer is a necessity. The head of a geological hammer is square at one end with chamfered edges, whilst at the other end it either tapers to a point or has a straight edge, usually at right angles to the shaft; some users prefer the chisel edge to be parallel to the shaft. A convenient general purpose weight for a geological hammer is about 1 kg (between 2 and 3 pounds). However, for breaking very hard rocks one may need a 3- or 6-kg (7- or 14-pound) head with a correspondingly longer and thicker shaft, whilst for the delicate work of trimming surplus matrix off specimens one uses a hammer weighing only about 0.25 kg (or only a few ounces). Similarly, one may need chisels of different widths and lengths.

Although the hammer is one of the geologist's essential tools, its use should paradoxically be avoided wherever possible. Firstly, the surface of an outcrop, particularly inland, is often differentially weathered to reveal internal structures which are not evident on the unweathered surface. Secondly, continual 'hammer erosion' may eventually completely destroy the outcrop, whilst the inevitable accumulation of angular debris can be harmful to farm animals and implements. Thirdly, especially when a party of inexperienced geologists is concerned, there is the danger of injury from flying pieces of rock.

A hammer is used for two main purposes. Firstly, it is often necessary to examine a fresh rock surface, to determine its composition and perhaps its structure. There is quite an art in using a hammer properly. Instead of just pounding on the rock, which usually only produces dust, one looks for a projecting corner, where the rock is likely to be relatively unweathered and strikes this off cleanly. Examine the specimen either with the naked eye or with a handlens ($\times 8$ and $\times 10$ being the most useful magnifications). Keep the lens as close to the eye as possible and then bring the rock into focus; do not hold rock and lens at arm's length. The details can often be seen more clearly if the specimen is wetted with the tongue or in water. With a party it is not usually necessary for everyone to make his own chip, which may not be typical of the rock. One chip, which shows the essential features, should be passed round. Secondly, the hammer is used, often with a cold chisel, to detach samples or blocks. Experience is necessary in selecting the best sample, both to provide one that is geologically useful and also that can be easily detached. On no account should one hammer be used as a chisel and hit on the head by a second; the temper of the steel is such that chips will fly off both heads very easily and dangerously. Cold chisels, sold by all ironmongers, should be used, for their steel has been tempered to give and not to chip.

Exposures of fossiliferous rocks suffer chiefly from the attacks of 'hammer-happy' geologists, followed by localities where prized mineral specimens have been found. Indiscriminate collecting may completely work out a locality, whilst the specimens obtained are scattered in private collections or even thrown away when the collector tires of them. As a result of too many cases of this, the specialist geologist wishing to collect for research purposes may find that material is very difficult to obtain; conversely, he may be very reluctant to publish details of such localities in excursion and field guides.

Hammers and chisels are, however, not the ideal tools when working in unconsolidated deposits, such as sand and clay. A broad bladed entrenching tool, obtainable from suppliers of camping equipment, is far more effective for cleaning up faces obscured by soil or vegetation, whilst a strong long-bladed knife or a gardener's bulb collecting trowel (or a builder's trowel with its end sharpened) are better for digging samples out of the face.

Labelling Specimens

Before moving off from an exposure, all specimens should be clearly labelled and securely packed. If this is not done (especially the labelling) and the specimens are not unpacked until some time has elapsed, there is the serious risk of errors being made as to the locality from which certain specimens came. Newspaper is the best material for the harder specimens, but fragile fossils may need to be packed in cotton wool and in small boxes. Where fossils have left impressions on both sides of a broken block or slab of rock, both should be carefully kept so that they can later be examined together. In some cases it may be wiser to bring away large blocks of fossiliferous rocks and break them up carefully at home or in the laboratory. Fossils from the geologically younger and therefore softer rocks, may need hardening treatment in the field, before they can be safely transported. This applies particularly to the remains of vertebrates. The locality, and if possible the exact horizon, of all specimens should be recorded. The safest way is to number each specimen and write the full details against the number in the field notebook. The number can be written on the specimen with a felt-tipped pen or on a piece of plaster or tape stuck on the specimen or a numbered ticket can be wrapped or packed up with the specimen.

The field notebook has to withstand hard usage, so stiff covers are essential. Clipboards are cumbersome, whilst individual sheets can easily become detached and lost. The field notebook should fit easily into one's pocket. The reporter style, opening at one end is to be recommended, for it is easier to use under bad weather conditions. The data recorded in the field notebook should be written at the place of observation. Under difficult conditions it is tempting to wait for a more comfortable situation to write up one's notes and field sketches. But memory is likely to be unreliable and points may occur to one that cannot be checked once the exposure has been left, so one must develop self-discipline. Geologists have been known to carry umbrellas, not for their own protection, but to give shelter when entering up their maps and notebooks!

The maps used in the field also need

to be protected. This can be done most simply by two pieces of hardboard, which also provide a firm surface for writing on. Pencils, including coloured pencils, a sharpener, a rubber and a ruler must also be carried. If a pen is used for note taking, make sure that its ink will not run or smudge if wetted.

Care and Safety During Field Work

Field work often takes one into ground that is potentially dangerous. When working on coasts, *always* first check the local tides, so as to avoid being cut off. Be careful not to dislodge loose blocks from cliffs and other high outcrops that may fall on you or other members of the party. In mountainous country, carry spare warm clothing, a whistle and a polythene survival bag and follow the advice given in the pamphlet *Mountain Safety* published by the Central Council for Physical Education. *Never explore unknown caves or abandoned mine workings on your own.* Go with properly equipped and experienced companions, having first informed a reliable person of your plans and anticipated time of return. Carry a first aid kit, particularly when leading a field party. At all times obey the Country Code, shutting gates, not damaging hedges or walls, leaving no litter, etc.

A Code for Geological Field Work

A geologist often wishes to enter private land (and this includes quarries, railway cuttings, road excavations, etc.) to visit exposures or to cross it on his way to moorland, coast sections, etc. It is essential to obtain permission to enter on any private land, even if this involves time and trouble in finding the owner.

One very serious result of the considerable increase in recent years of those engaged in field work is that the bad behaviour of a small minority has had serious repercussions. Undoubtedly geologists have, at times, been blamed for the misdoings of others, but there are far too many well proven cases in which geologists were at fault. One farmer literally blew up a certain exposure to stop geologists crossing his land to visit it! Some land owners (including quarry owners) have been so enraged by thoughtless damage that they now refuse access to *all* geologists; others will not allow hammers to be brought on to their property. It is particularly important when visiting working quarries to make sure that all safety regulations, including the wearing of hard hats, are complied with and that both the arrival and departure of the party are reported.

The Geologists' Association with the support of all other leading British geological societies has drawn up a *Code for Geological Field Work.* Copies can be obtained from:

The Librarian,
Geologists' Association,
c/o Geology Department,
University College of London,
Gower Street,
London WC1E 6BT, England

Anyone leading a party or engaged in field work on his own, should obtain a copy of the Code and follow it.

'Let no one regret your visit' is a motto that should be kept in mind by anyone carrying out field work, geological or otherwise.

'Reading' Exposures

On entering a large exposure, it is a great mistake to walk straight up to the face and hammer it furiously. One should always stand back and 'read' its main features: the dip of the beds, whether there is any evidence of faulting or of folding, of unconformity, of channelling or whether any particular stratum shows very distinctive characters. If igneous rocks are known or suspected to be present, are any contacts visible? It is surprising how often the beginner in field work may miss the really significant features of an exposure by rushing up to the face and not looking beyond that small part. The adage of 'not being able to see the wood for the trees' should never be forgotten by a geologist. One has frequently noticed that when a party of geologists has entered a quarry, listened to the leader's remarks and then been let free to examine it, it is the more experienced members of the party who have walked straight to the most interesting part, whilst the rest were strung out haphazardly along the face. It was only too apparent who had been 'reading' the face, whilst listening to the leader, and who had not.

It is also good training in field work to ask the members of a party to take turns in 'reading' exposures. If different 'readings' for the same exposure are suggested, these provide hypotheses to be tested by closer examination. The criteria for testing each hypothesis will also need to be discussed.

'Reading' the exposure also enables one to plan the best way to examine it in the time available. The objectives of field work may differ. If one is making a survey of the area, then one must consider and attempt to interpret, all the features shown. If, on the other hand, one is studying the palaeontology or the depositional history or the igneous or the structural history or the drift geology of the area, one naturally concentrates on these features, but surely not to the exclusion of everything else.

Critical Exposures

Many significant sedimentological, igneous or structural features (erosive junctions, graded bedding, chilled margins, etc.) seem obvious enough when described in the classroom and illustrated by photographs of clear examples. The beginner in field work is only too often disconcerted to find that it is quite another matter in the field. It may be necessary to work over (indeed crawl over) many outcrops before one finds the critical exposure that gives, for example, unmistakable evidence by truncated foresets (No. 19) or by graded bedding (No. 35) or by bedding/cleavage relationships (Nos 78, 79) of the direction of 'younging' in folded rocks. In the other exposures, the beds may have been of too uniform lithology or the subsequent tectonic stress may have obliterated original slight changes in lithology or recent weathering may not have etched out sufficiently the sought-for features. When such a critical exposure has been found, the features shown should be carefully recorded. *On no account* damage it by hammering, but leave it for the enjoyment and interest of other geologists. The same remarks, of course, apply to the preservation of critical exposures showing other important features, such as igneous contacts, evidence of polyphase folding or significant sedimentary features.

The Field Notebook

The field notebook should contain full details of each day's work, the route followed and the observations made, both at and between exposures. Some years hence you may wish to revisit the area, but it is never safe to rely solely on memory, or another geologist may wish to follow exactly the route that you have taken.

The National Grid overprinted on the British Ordnance Survey sheets provides the best and most concise means of recording the position of exposures. With a 6-figure reference, the exposure is somewhere within a square of 100 metre sides and with an 8-figure reference the sides of the square are reduced to 10 metres, but to determine an 8-figure grid reference one needs a base map of the scale of 1/25,000 or larger. If one is using a base map without such a grid overprinted on it, locations can be given by distance and compass direction or whole circle bearing from some easily identifiable point, e.g. 200m W.N.W. (285°) of Aldermaston Church. If a printed place name has to be used, underline the letter chosen as the measuring point, e.g. 500m N.E. (45°) of ALDERMASTON. It is, however, advisable to use printed place names as reference points only as a last resort, for their location and the style of printing used may not be the same on the different editions of a topographic sheet.

During the passage of years there will have been changes. Some exposures, especially working quarries, will have altered, others may have disappeared, owing to dumping and other causes, and new exposures may have been opened. The state of many coastal sections, especially on the softer rocks, is largely determined by the extent of cliff falls and land slides. A heavy gale may scour the sand off a beach and uncover, for a short time, deposits that are normally obscured. It is valuable to know precisely what was visible on a particular date.

When one is engaged in geological mapping (see p. 27) the position is somewhat different, for both the notebook and large scale map are available for the recording of observations and their precise location.

Field Sketching

Adequately labelled field sketches are often the most effective way of recording observations. Field sketches do not require great artistic gifts, but rather the ability to analyse ('read') a section and to record clearly its salient geological features, to record significant pieces of detail or to 'read' a view and appreciate its geological make-up. They must be clear and not messy and over-elaborate. But at the same time they must be accurate and, at least approximately to scale. As shown on Fig. 27 the height and length of the exposure and also its compass direction must be shown. These distances may only be estimated, but this is better than giving no idea of size at all. For more accurate work, the height of the section and the thickness of the individual beds exposed must be measured. Elaborate surveying equipment is not necessary. Much can be done with an extensible steel rule, a graduated walking stick or even a scale cut into the hammer shaft.

Do not rely on photographs in the hope that sketches can be made from them at a later date. Apart from the uncertainties of lighting and of weather, it is surprising how many photographs taken in the field prove to be disappointing in showing geological detail at all clearly. Many rocks are shades of red or brown. The human eye can detect subtle differences in this colour range much better than most colour films, and certainly better than all black-and-white films. The camera is also not selective and must record the vegetation, etc., that is obscuring parts of the geology. Irrelevant detail of this kind can be omitted from a sketch (compare No. 18 and Fig. 22). Photographs of landscapes, taken without special lenses and filters, too often appear flat and uninteresting. Good clear photographs, including post cards, are excellent for illustrating reports and other accounts of the area, but it is far better to rely on the field notebook rather than the camera for keeping a full coverage of the geological features seen during the day. Also having to decide what are the significant points to be shown on a field sketch 'concentrates one's mind wonderfully', far more so than pointing the camera in the right general direction and clicking the shutter.

Sketch plans should be made of large exposures, such as quarries and the position of the faces sketched and of the smaller pieces of detail marked on the plan. This will save much time on future visits to the quarry either by yourself or by someone else using your notebook. Details of the thickness and nature of the various beds exposed can be written (in abbreviated form) if there is room against the sketch or the beds can be numbered and each one described on another page. It is a geological convention to number the beds in their order of deposition, so in uninverted beds, the lowest one exposed will be No. 1 or A and so on (e.g. No. 35, Fig. 25). If fossils have been found, record whether they were found *in situ* in a particular layer or layers or whether they were picked up loose from talus.

The sketches on pp. 154–202 relating to many of the colour plates show how the significant features of many types of geological phenomena can be sketched with a minimum of lines.

Landscape sketching can be of two types, either an extensive view (Fig. 44) or detail, such as the form of a hill or ridges offset by a fault or an overflow channel or other morphological feature. When sketching a coastal view, the dip of the beds will usually be visible in the cliffs, but inland, there may be no clear exposures, so that the features to be emphasized are the scarp-forming beds and the intervening strike vales together with any marked changes in the form of the ground produced by the outcropping of beds of a different character, such as upfaulted or intrusive igneous rocks. The profile of a hill will reflect the nature and inclination of the beds that form it, the changes in vegetation and of land form along the junction of beds of contrasting lithology, e.g. limestone and shale or sand and clay can be recorded by a sketch.

Whilst sketches are best drawn in

pencil in the field, they will be more permanent if inked-in afterwards, preferably on the same evening when they are fresh in one's mind.

If the notebook is to be used afterwards for writing a report or revisiting the area, much time will be saved in the long run, if the book is paginated; also it is well worth maintaining an index at the back of the notebook in order to enter such items as sketches made, photographs taken, and lists of fossils and other specimens collected.

Field Identification

Precise identification of rocks, minerals or fossils is often impossible in the field, even with the help of a hand lens. This applies particularly to fossils, which may be partially hidden by matrix or smeared over with mud. Specimens must be brought back to the laboratory for cleaning and for consultation of the appropriate reference books for full identification. The field record of brachiopod, productid, etc., can then be amended to generic and perhaps specific level. 'Spot' identifications in the field may well be incorrect, and if not checked by later study, such identifications may lead to erroneous conclusions.

Good specimens of the commoner minerals can usually be identified in the field from their physical and crystallographic characters, but poor specimens may need more thorough examination in the laboratory – and there is always the possibility of finding a rare mineral which one has not encountered before.

There may well be difficulties in the identification of rocks under field conditions. The chemical changes due to weathering may completely change the colour of the rock (Chapter 7). If one is faced with a strange rock type one must first determine whether it is of sedimentary, igneous or metamorphic origin. Examine the specimen from every angle, so as to find the clearest face for study and, if necessary, use the hammer to expose a fresh (unweathered) surface. Then attempt to assign the specimen to the appropriate group of sedimentary, igneous or metamorphic rocks. If the specimen has been collected *in situ*, the general features of the exposure will often be helpful in determining its category. But this cannot apply if the specimen has been picked up loose on a beach or pulled out of a face of boulder clay or a river gravel.

As with fossils, do not be over-precise. Even with the coarse-grained igneous rocks, it is often difficult to determine the exact nature of the coloured minerals, not to mention the feldspars. A general identification as a granitic or a gabbroic rock may well be as far as one can go with an identification in the field. Its detailed mineralogical composition, leading to a more precise name, can only be determined by studying a thin section under a petrological microscope. With the finer grained igneous rocks, precision in field identification is correspondingly more difficult and is a matter of experience. The essential mineral to look for is quartz; if present the rock will be acidic, if absent more basic. Unfortunately, quartz is one of the more difficult minerals to recognize. Before going into the field, it is a good plan to work carefully through a representative collection of different types of igneous rocks, so as to train one's eye in the detection of quartz.

If an exposure shows several types of igneous rock, one cutting another, it is a mistake to think that each must be accurately identified in the field. Sketch their relationships carefully and do not be ashamed of labelling the sketch 'Granite A cutting Granite B'. The two granites can be named more precisely after specimens of them have been studied in the laboratory.

The mineralogical composition of some metamorphic rocks, especially gneisses and schists, may similarly be difficult to determine and 'field' names may have to be used.

The sedimentary rocks can usually be identified with greater precision in the field, including those that are transitional between the main groups, e.g. sandy limestone. Study of the average size and the variation in size of the quartz grains of the arenaceous rocks enables one to distinguish between say a 'well graded medium sand or sandstone' and a 'poorly graded sand or sandstone with scattered pebbles'. Colour can also be used, though this may vary with the state of weathering of the rock. If calcareous rocks are expected to be encountered, it is helpful to carry a well protected dropper-type bottle of dilute hydrochloric acid. Any limestone, except a dolomitic limestone, will effervesce to a few drops of the acid. This is a more reliable test than seeing if the suspected limestone can be scratched with the hammer or a pocket knife. A non-calcareous clayey matrix will scratch just as easily as calcite, but it will not react to the acid. The acid bottle is equally useful in areas of metamorphic rocks which may include marbles. Uncompacted sandy clays and pure clays can be distinguished by fingering. If quartz grains are present, they will feel rough to the touch, whilst a pure clay can be moulded into shape by gentle pressure. The plant remains, stems, roots, etc., of carbonaceous rocks are usually easily recognizable, whilst the rock salt (halite) of evaporite deposits is recognizable by its taste and gypsum by being scratched with one's finger nail.

Compass and Clinometer

It is essential to record, not only the nature of the rock bodies, but also their geometry. This requires measuring their dip – the maximum inclination and its direction on the bedding planes, joint planes. foliation planes, etc. – and the direction of strike – a horizontal line on such planes. The direction of strike must be at right angles to that of the dip (Fig. 1a).

These directions are measured with a compass – a prismatic or similar type for precise work – though it should be remembered that most geological surfaces are not truly planar: they may be curved or slightly irregular, and the reading made is only likely to be accurate to within a few degrees. The direction of strike (Fig. 1, AOB), or dip (OD) is best recorded as a whole circle (360°) bearing from true north, so allowance has to be made for magnetic declination, that is the angle between bearings of true and magnetic north. In 1975 magnetic north in Britain was about 7° west of true north, decreasing by about ½° each eight years, so that 7° must be subtracted from all magnetic bearings to give true north bearings. On some

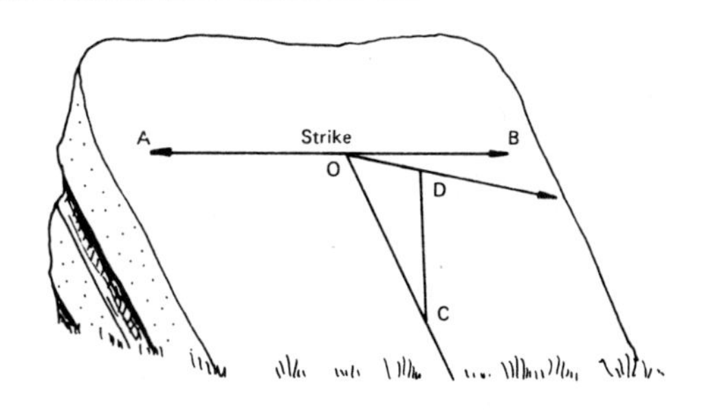

a

b

Fig. 1. a *Strike and dip readings on a bedding plane.* b *Measurement of pitch, plunge and trend of a linear structure.*

compasses allowance can be made for the declination, so that readings are given directly as bearings from true north.

The amount of dip (angle DOC) is measured with a clinometer. In its simplest form this consists of a protractor with a small weight at the end of a thread or a swinging pointer attached to its index point. When the protractor is placed on an inclined surface, the thread or pointer will hang vertical and so the tilt of the surface can be measured in degrees. Such a simple instrument is unlikely to survive long under field conditions unless the protractor face and the pointer are protected by clear perspex. More elaborate (and expensive) clinometers are combined with an accurate compass, so that the one instrument can be used for determining both strike and dip.

These measurements should be recorded on the map where possible, and also in the notebook, in a standardized form (Fig. 3). This can be done conveniently in the notebook as on the map using the symbols, drawing them in the book with north as the top of the page and the symbol in approximately its correct orientation. Thus bedding with a strike of 045° and a dip of 45° to the south-east can be recorded as ↘ 45, or as a bar drawn along the direction of strike with a tick on the downdip side and the amount of dip against that, ⨯ 45. Strike bars are more effective on the map, for they show clearly any change in the run of the beds, and must in any case be used when the beds are vertical.

It must be emphasized that the true dip is the *maximum* inclination of the bedding plane or any other plane to the horizontal. The true dip may not always be easily determinable. If a long narrow curved working, such as a railway cutting (Fig. 2), exposes a uniformly dipping bed, the inclination of the bed as seen in the sides of the cutting will vary from zero, that is the bed appears to be horizontal, where the direction of the cutting is along the strike of the bed, through varying amounts of *apparent* dip, until a maximum is reached where the line of the cutting coincides with the direction of true dip. However, if the walls of the cutting are not vertical everywhere, it should be possible to find places where sufficiently large areas of bedding planes are exposed. The direction of horizontal lines on them (the strike) can then be determined by the use of either a spirit level and compass or a suitable compass/clinometer. The direction of strike and the amount and direction of true dip would be the same wherever they were measured along the curved cutting.

Dip measurements should therefore only be taken where one can find a surface on which the strike can be determined. This may not always be possible, especially where rock faces are vertical, as in deep quarries, on sheer cliffs or mountain sides. In such situations one must measure the *apparent* dip and record it as such.

Good places for acquiring facility in the use of compass and clinometer are exposures in strongly current bedded strata or those showing folded beds on a wave cut platform (No. 76). In the first case, there will be appreciable variation in the readings taken in a large exposure, due to

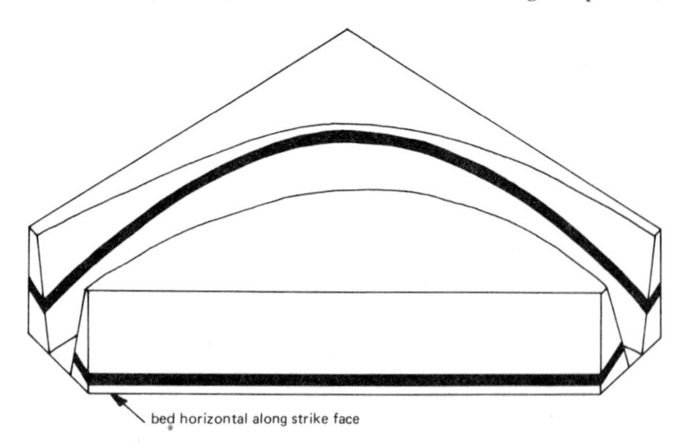

Fig. 2. *Block diagram of a curved cutting in dipping strata.*

fluctuations in the strength and direction of the depositing currents, whether aqueous or aeolian. These readings can then be plotted as a rose or other form of diagram which will show clearly both the mean direction of the current bedding and also variations from the mean. Such a diagram will emphasize how misleading a single dip reading in these beds might be. The data obtained could also provide material for further statistical studies. The measurements taken on the folded rocks on the shore will provide the data for working out the geometrical form of the folds.

If a rock surface bears a linear structure, such as the striations on a fault plane, or flute casts on a bedding plane, the angle with the strike can be measured *on the surface* as an angle of *pitch* in a particular direction (Fig. 1b, angle AOE). A linear structure can also be regarded as a line in space, regardless of whether it lies on a planar surface. Indeed, it may lie on a curved surface, such as the axis of a fold (Fig. 17a) along the zone of sharpest curvature on a bedding plane. In this case the line will have a trend (unless it is vertical), which may be thought of as the strike (the direction OF) of an imaginary vertical plane passing through the line (OFE in the diagram), and a *plunge*, which is the angle of inclination from the horizontal of the line in this vertical plane (angle FOE). Note that the direction of this plunge must be recorded: on an east–west line it could be either to the east or the west.

As with the measurements of a planar surface, those of linear structures can be recorded in the notebook using the standard symbols (Fig. 3).

When working in areas of strongly folded beds or of metamorphosed rocks, compass/clinometers are in constant use to measure and record not only the dip and strike of the bedding planes (where recognizable), but also such features as cleavage (No. 73), foliation (No. 142), lineation (No. 142) and fold axes (No. 76). Indeed, for specialist work, any directional or planar features that can be measured and recorded on the map. From the analysis of such data one hopes to be able to deduce the succession and nature of the geological events that have deformed the area.

The Systematic Examination of Exposures

As already mentioned (p. 16), the ability to read exposures also enables one to plan the best method of examining each one thoroughly and of recording one's observations. A sound general rule is to follow the geological history, working from the oldest to the youngest.

For example, if an unconformity is exposed, first sketch it from a distance. Then examine in their order of deposition, the beds beneath the unconformity, recording their lithology, thickness, fossil content (if any), dip and any other structural features (faults, etc.) which are cut off at the surface of unconformity. Record, perhaps in the form of a sketch, any particularly significant pieces of detail. Then concentrate on the surface of unconformity. Is it a plane and does it rest on a bored surface cut across the underlying strata (No. 18)? Is there any evidence of weathering of the beds beneath it? Is it a markedly irregular surface with a coarse basement conglomerate or even a breccia above it (No. 4)? In the first case the beds above the unconformity must rest on a plane of marine erosion; in the second they were very probably deposited on a land surface of low relief and in the third case much more rapidly on a deeply dissected surface. Then treat the beds above the unconformity in the same way, noting, in particular, any faults or dykes which are clearly post-unconformity. Finally, examine the top few feet of the exposure to see if there are any drift deposits overlying the solid rocks and if so, what is their nature and under what conditions might they have been formed.

By following such a systematic approach it is unlikely that any significant features will have been missed, whilst at the same time the geological history of the beds present will have been deduced.

As one visits adjacent exposures or perhaps works along a coast section, one keeps in mind a clear picture of the unconformity and of the beds above and below it. Any changes in its nature or the appearance of additional beds in the succession will be quickly recognized. In the notebook one can record either that there was no significant change from the first exposure or the occurrence of the new evidence.

Similarly, if an exposure shows a granite intruded into country rock with dykes cutting both the granite and the country rock, one would first examine and record the characters of the granite and of the country rock. Then one can study their contact, looking particularly at such features as any chilling of the granite towards the contact and the development of new minerals in the country rock. Then examine the dykes, especially their margins, and finally any drift deposits. If there are a number of nearby exposures in the country rock at varying distances from the granite margin, then a comparison of the features visible in them should enable one to trace the increasing effects of thermal metamorphism as shown by the changes in the nature, the grain size and the mineral content of the country rock as one approaches nearer and nearer to the granite.

The complexities of regionally metamorphosed rocks are perhaps a matter for the geologist with considerable field experience, but he too will analyse his exposures thoroughly in an attempt to deduce the sequence of changes that have affected the rocks.

Planning Field Work

Field work is far more interesting if it is planned to develop and illustrate a definite theme. One possibility is a dip-traverse, preferably on foot, across a variety of rock-types, so that each unit and its topographical expression can be studied in turn. The day's work can then be summarized in a section or sections which will also show the structure of the country that has been crossed. Much knowledge should also have been gained, preferably by guided group discussion rather than from pronouncements by the leader, of the geological history of the area. Alternatively, lateral changes in the characters of certain beds might be studied in a number of exposures along their strike. In this case, the day's work can best be summarized by comparative vertical sections of the exposures visited. Another possible theme might be the unconformable and overstepping relationships of different strata against an upstanding or 'positive' block. The objective would be to trace, if only very much in outline, the extent of the successive marine transgressions across it. In heavily drift covered country, it may be possible to plan a route along the edge of a sheet of boulder clay. The erratics found would provide not only good practice in rock identification, but also discussion of the areas across which the ice sheet might have travelled. One would also hope to be able to include such features as overflow channels, diverted streams, drumlins, moraines, etc. Even in the built-up areas of central London, one can trace the extent of the various terraces of the River Thames, comparing level streets on the terraces with those which are gently sloping – for these are built across the now very degraded bluffs that mark the front or riverward edge of each terrace flat. One would also hope to be fortunate enough to find temporary exposures in the terrace gravels. The changes to be looked for as one crosses the aureole of a granite or other large body of igneous rock have already been mentioned (p. 24). The contrasts between sills, acid and basic lava flows, volcanic necks, etc., could be the subject of interesting field work in an area that has suffered a volcanic episode.

These are examples of field excursions with a definite theme that are surely more interesting and rewarding than a car- or coach-borne chase across country, stopping to look briefly at a number of virtually unrelated exposures.

The theme should be allowed to develop gradually during the day as discussion of the observations made at successive exposures builds up into a picture. At the end of the day, the leader can summarize the story that has developed, making comparison, where appropriate, with what has been seen on other excursions.

Between Exposures

So far we have been considering the examination of exposures. But it is a poor 'geologist' who can only deduce the nature of the rocks and the structure of the country over which he is working from what is exposed. Over the greater part of the land areas of the Earth exposure is anything but 100%, the solid rocks being masked to varying degrees by vegetation, by ice sheets and glaciers, by blown sand and other types of drift deposits, not to mention man's activities.

The geologist must therefore train his eye to read not only the exposures, but also the ground between exposures. He must note and consider the significance of the changes, often but slight changes, in the form of the ground. The reason may be human (a Neolithic barrow, a grassed mound once crowned by a wooden Norman castle or some later building, an abandoned and partially filled in quarry, even a bomb crater), or it may be of natural origin. If natural, does it relate to a cover of drift deposits or to the nature of the solid rocks? A marked change in the vegetation cover may also be significant, especially if it occurs where the nature of the soil also alters. We shall be discussing such topics more fully in the section on Geological Mapping

(p. 27), but would emphasize here that the interest of field excursions of the kind described in the preceeding section will be greatly increased if observations are made and recorded whilst walking from one exposure to the next.

For example, during the dip traverse one should try to determine as precisely as possible where one walked from one rock unit on to another, so that the limits of each rock unit's outcrop can be shown accurately in the section. In areas of gently dipping strata, differential erosion will have etched out the slight differences in their character, with the more resistant layers outcropping as cuestas, with steep scarp face up-dip and the gently dipping dipslope behind it, whilst belts of lower ground or strike vales occur along the strike of the less resistant beds. If the resistant layer is hundreds of metres in thickness, like the Upper Cretaceous Chalk or the more important Jurassic limestones of western Europe, its scarp face will be a line of impressive hills and the dipslope behind many kilometres in width, whilst a resistant bed only a metre or so in thickness will give rise to only a faint low feature but of the same cross profile. On the dip traverse one should therefore try to determine where the base of each resistant bed outcrops along the foot of its scarp or feature and the end of its dipslope, where the top of this unit passes under beds of a different lithology. As mentioned more fully later (p. 27), it may not be possible on just one traverse across them to locate the positions of these junctions exactly, but one should attempt to do this. If the beds are folded, this will be apparent from the form of the ground, for the scarp faces on either side of a dissected anticline will face towards each other in contrast to the inward facing dipslopes of a synclinal structure. The abrupt ending and offsetting of a feature must be due to faulting.

During the traverse along the strike of the bed, attention should also be paid to its topographic expression. Are the changes in lithology visible in the exposures reflected by variations in the height and character of the feature that it forms?

Any evidence as to the presence and the nature of drift deposits should not be ignored. If river terraces are crossed during the dip traverse, this should be shown not only by the gravelly soil, but also by their topographic form (see p. 25). Landslipping may have taken place along the foot of the major scarps, to form hummocky ground with large cracks. The larger blocks that have slid downhill will form low features, often markedly arcuate in plan, whilst any rocks exposed will probably be dipping back into the hillside at a high angle (Fig. 5c). The limits of such foundered ground are usually easily recognizable. The contact of the granite will most probably occur in an upland area of irregular topography. Patches of peat on the ridge tops should be easily recognized from their waterlogged character (except in very dry weather) their characteristic soil and vegetation. The edges of any depression infilled with boulder clay will be marked not only by the changes in the nature of the grass, but also by the steepening of the ground round a flat or nearly flat area.

2 GEOLOGICAL MAPPING

The ultimate test of a field geologist is his ability to make a geological map of an area – a map showing the outcrop of the different beds, the position of faults, mineral veins, etc., together with measurements of dip, cleavage, foliation, etc., so that the structure of the area can be worked out. There is usually little difficulty in doing this where the solid rocks are completely exposed, though progress may be slow if the structures are complex and many different rock-types are involved. However, deciding on the exact position of geological boundaries is much more difficult where exposures are few owing to the cover of vegetation, buildings, etc. Finally, in thick forest the geologist may be restricted to the few places where rivers and streams have cut deep enough to expose the solid rocks. Away from the stream courses, pits may have to be sunk to expose bedrock, a time consuming and expensive process.

Another important factor is the extent to which the solid rocks are hidden by unconsolidated deposits. Where this drift cover is extensive, for example great spreads of boulder clay and fluvio–glacial outwash material, accurate mapping of the limits of the solid rocks is impossible without knowledge of the beds penetrated by boreholes sunk for water supply and for other purposes, and it is to be hoped that these boreholes are not too widely spaced. The Geological Survey of Great Britain (now the Institute of Geological Sciences) recognizes this by publishing two different geological sheets for those areas where there is much drift: the *Drift Edition* which shows the extent of the drifts and also where the solid rocks project through the drift or are exposed in the bottom of valleys, and the *Solid Edition* showing where the solid rocks would outcrop if the drift cover had been removed. The first is of value to those, such as civil engineers, agriculturalists, etc., who are interested in the kind of beds that actually underlie the surface of the ground, the other for miners and others who are concerned with the deeper seated disposition of the strata. For areas where there is only a limited amount of drift, so that the run of the solid rocks is not significantly hidden, only one edition – *Solid with Drift* – is published.

We are writing here for those who are learning to construct their own geological map. They would be well advised to choose an area of the Solid with Drift type, an area of varied rock-types, not highly metamorphosed or structurally too complex, an area also without extensive woodland or that is too much built up.

First Steps

For anything other than reconnaissance mapping, one must have as base map a topographic map on the scale of 1:25,000 or preferably 1:10,000. It will take a little practice to become adept at locating one's exact position on such a large scale map. In lowland country this should not be too difficult, for on a 1:10,000 map every building, field boundary, bend in a road, etc., is shown, so one should normally be able to locate one's position by eye estimation of some nearby point. But if the topographic background is not sufficiently detailed, or as sometimes happens, there have been changes since the ground was topographically surveyed, then one must use pacing on a compass direction to fix one's position. Contour lines are also helpful, but it must be appreciated that they do not always 'fit' the ground precisely. If one is working in an unenclosed upland area with few roads, tracks or buildings and with only widely spaced contours above the 1000ft level, locating oneself accurately may be a much more difficult matter. This is particularly the case if the topographic maps were surveyed many years ago. Such ground is best left to the specialist, who has the time and experience to determine his place of observation by compass or sextant resection, by plane tabling, etc. Vertical aerial photographs are often of great help as they may well show much more detail than the topographic map. One can locate one's position more easily and then record one's observations either on the photograph, or better, on tracing paper placed over the photograph. But remember that there may be distortion towards the margin of each photograph.

It must also be appreciated that it takes time to get one's eye trained to recognize subtle variations in the rocks and in the form of the ground. It is a good plan to spend some time walking over the area, locating the larger exposures, studying them thoroughly, so as to work out the succession of the beds present and also to familiarize oneself with the characteristics of the different rock units that one hopes to trace across country. Until one's eye is thoroughly trained, it helps to carry representatives of the various rock types for comparison with the somewhat puzzling fragments one may dig out of ditches, rabbit holes, etc. It is also advisable to choose the most straightforward part of the area as the best place in which to start the mapping. The more complicated parts should not be attempted until one is thoroughly familiar with the rock types present and the problems that they pose.

Hard and Dotted Boundaries

With a well sharpened pencil one can draw a line 0.5mm (1/50 inch) in width. On a map on the scale of 1:50,000, such a line covers a strip of ground 25m (28yds) in width, that is just over the length of a tennis court. On a 1:25,000 map, the thickness of the line is more than the width of a tennis court and on the British '6 inch' (1:10,560) map about 5m (6yds). These figures show the limits of accuracy within which one should try to determine the position of a geological boundary on the ground, so that its exact position can be recorded on the map by a 0.5mm thick pencil line. If the boundary is completely exposed, e.g. in a quarry, in a stream section or in closely spaced crags up a hillside, one can place it accurately on the ground and hence record it precisely on the map. However, where the exposure ends and one has to trace, or attempt to trace, the boundary across fields or other unexposed ground, it can be a very different matter. Walk a few hundred metres from the exposure and one's margin of uncertainty as to where to place the boundary may well be the width or even the length of a tennis court.

A topographic map is a matter of observation only, for the topographic surveyor recorded only what he could see (the position of houses, hedges, etc.). The geological surveyor has to use both observation and inference, for he has to show on the topographical background the position of the geological boundaries as accurately as he could locate them when he was on the ground. Wherever the boundary could be accurately determined, he should draw a firm (continuous) line, for in such places he was as confident as the topographical surveyor. Where, through lack of evidence he was uncertain and the limits of his uncertainty were greater than the width on the ground of his line on the map, he should draw a dotted (broken) line. Anyone in the future who is using this geological map can then see where the map can be regarded as accurate and where he should allow for some margin of uncertainty. This is particularly important where the geological map is being used for some engineering or commercial purpose. Also, in the future, another geologist walking across the same ground, may be fortunate enough to find exposures, often of a temporary nature (pipelines, excavations for buildings, road widening, etc.) that provide the evidence for correcting parts of a dotted boundary and converting it into a firm one. Everyone making a geological map should show by using firm and dotted lines appropriately, how precisely he was able to locate his boundaries on the ground in relation to the scale of the map that he was using.

Recording One's Evidence

All the evidence on which one's map is based must be recorded either on the field map or in the field notebook. These must be used in combination. One should also become familiar with the normal conventional symbols (Fig. 3) and use them. If one is using a 1 : 10,000 base map and the exposures and other mapping evidence are not too close together, it may be possible to record all one's observations (in abbreviated and symbolic form) on the face of the map. But if this would cause overcrowding, one can number each place of observation and then enter the details in the field notebook against the number or alternatively use a pin to prick a hole through the map at the correct place and then on the back of the map write the observations against the numbered pinhole. When the report on the area is being written up, one has to balance the disadvantage of having to consult both map and notebook against having all the information on the map, but much of it on the back.

The observations entered on the map in pencil in the field must be made permanent, using a fine pen and ink that will not run if wetted. It is far wiser to make a practice of inking in each day's work the same evening. It is fresh in one's mind, which may be as well if parts of one's notes or even boundaries happen to be rather illegible. Inking-in can certainly be done when the weather is too bad for field work, but it is a bad habit to leave it until there is a break in the weather. One's memory becomes more and more treacherous and the weather may continue fine!

Fig. 3. *Symbols for use in geological mapping.*

Neat penmanship is clearly an asset to the geological mapper and, if necessary, must be acquired by practice. Do not forget to include in one's field equipment an adequate supply of pencils of different hardnesses, pencil sharpener, eraser, mapping pens and inks, together with ruler, scale and protractor. Some geologists prefer to use different coloured inks for the different types of boundaries and observations, e.g. those for solid rocks in black, faults in red, and features in blue. Others like to make an ink line round each exposure of a bed and then to paint these with a strong shade of the appropriate colour. A distinctly paler wash is then used for the remaining (unexposed) parts of the bed's outcrop. This technique certainly shows clearly how well or otherwise a particular bed is exposed.

'Soft-rock' and 'Hard-rock' Geology

Geologists often use the colloquial expressions 'soft-rock' and 'hard-rock' to distinguish between two slightly different lines of approach to the problems of constructing a geological map. A *soft-rock geologist* works on the beds of Tertiary and Mesozoic age, rocks which in the British Isles and indeed most of Europe away from the Pyrenees, Alps, Carpathians and other Young Mountain Chains, have not been subjected to orogenic stress. Since their deposition, these beds may have undergone lithification and diagenetic changes, but they are completely unmetamorphosed. Dips are usually gentle, so differences in hardness have been etched out to produce scarpland topography, often of no great relief. The Pleistocene ice sheets spread across much of these lowlands, so that over wide areas the solid rocks are masked by drift deposits of glacial or fluvial origin.

A *hard-rock geologist* is one who works on the beds of Palaeozoic and Pre-Cambrian age, which have been affected by the Variscan and older orogenies. The beds he studies have been folded, contorted and metamorphosed to varying degrees as well as intruded by granites and other igneous bodies. The beds thus hardened and compacted typically form upland areas, whose relief has often been accentuated by the scouring effects of the Pleistocene ice sheets. Drift deposits are likely to be restricted to the bottoms and sides of the valleys. Crags and boulders mark the outcrop of the harder units.

The distinction between soft-rock and hard-rock areas is not solely in terms of the age of the rocks. Except in the extreme south-west (Cornubia), the Upper Palaeozoic rocks of the British Isles were not seriously affected by the Variscan Orogeny, so over large areas of England, Wales and the Midland Valley of Scotland, they too produce scarpland topography, often of considerable relief, with the outcrops of the harder layers showing as lines of rocky 'scars'. The less compacted sandstones and limestones of Mesozoic and Tertiary age do not usually protrude through the turf.

Mapping on Soft-rocks

The soft-rock geologist is therefore usually faced with a serious lack of natural exposures, though quarries, road cuts and other man-made openings are likely to be more numerous than in the upland regions. In between these he must search for his evidence. On the other hand, the beds over which he is working may be soft enough for him to make his own exposures by screwing into the ground an auger, essentially an oversized bradawl. This will penetrate through the soil and subsoil to reach, often at a depth of about a metre, the underlying sand or clay. When the auger is withdrawn, a sample will be retained in the spiral at its end. But augering, especially to depths of several metres, is both a slow business and also hard physical work. One soon learns that it is unwise to screw down too far before trying to pull the auger up. If one does, the auger just stays fast. It is better to work in short lengths and also to plan one's augering campaign so as to avoid, as far as possible, the sinking of unnecessary holes. But closely spaced augering may be the only way of tracing accurately a sand/clay junction across farmland, especially pasture fields. The holes, 2–3cm or less in diameter, with the normal screw auger, should be filled in afterwards to prevent any possibility of damage to stock. Augering is also used to obtain samples from peat bogs, silted-up lake basins, coastal mud flats, etc. The object here is to obtain profile samples for subsequent laboratory study of pollen content, mineralogical composition, grading, etc. The augers used are not of the screw types, but are designed to bring up as undisturbed a sample as possible (Nos. 154, 155).

Tracing Features

Much can be learnt by tracing the run of the features formed by the more resistant layers. The scarps of the thicker units are usually obvious enough, more difficult to follow are the low features made by the thinner beds. Also these must not be confused with old cultivation terraces of man-made origin. Such lynchets are usually straight, often part of a definite pattern and tend to decrease in height and merge into the general slope, unlike the more persistent and often gently curving natural features. Low features can be seen more easily when they are lit by the slanting rays of the rising or setting sun rather than when the sun is overhead. It is also important to look carefully at a piece of ground from different directions, for slight but significant changes of slope may be more apparent when viewed from a certain angle.

Mark on the map the position of the change or changes of slope at the foot of the scarp features, any marked changes of slope along the face of a major scarp and also at the termination of dip slopes. But these features may not always coincide with the geological boundaries (Fig. 4). So the next step is to walk slowly along each feature searching for any evidence as to where the change in the nature of the beds actually occurs. One may be fortunate and find the base of the feature-forming unit exposed by a stream flowing down the scarp or in a deep cut track or lane. Springs will be thrown out at or just above the base of a sandstone or a limestone resting on clay or shale. The major springs will have been noted by the topographical surveyor and marked on the large scale map. In between these the position of the spring line may be indicated by the growth of rushes and other moisture loving plants and by small seepages of water. Look closely at the soil on fields and particularly at that thrown out by badgers, foxes, rabbits and even the humble mole. Beds containing distinctive pebbles, such as phosphatic nodules, can be traced across the fields by noting the uphill limit of such pebbles in the soil. Augering is unlikely to be helpful at

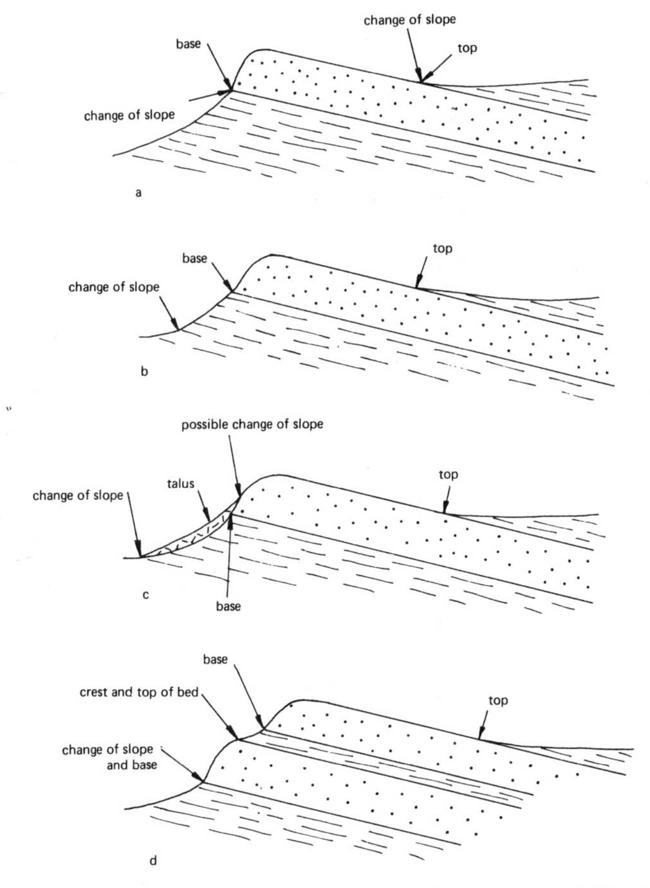

Fig. 4. *Features in relation to geological boundaries. The more resistent bed is stippled in each figure.* a *Base of resistent bed coincident with change of slope.* b *Change of slope below base of bed.* c *Mantle of scree or talus obscuring base of bed.* d *Double scarp.*

the foot of a major scarp, for there is likely to be too great a thickness of downwash to be penetrated by an auger of normal length.

If one can find definite evidence as to the position of the geological boundary relative to the change of slope, then one can record a firm boundary on the map. Otherwise one can only mark a dotted boundary along the foot of the feature.

The soft-rock geologist is always trying to see through the vegetation cover, so high summer is not really the best time for mapping. True the days are long, but so are the crops, the grass and the weeds. One must not damage crops by walking over them once they have started vigorous growth. One also tends to get rather tired of forcing one's way through dense nettles, brambles, thorn, etc., to see whether or not they are hiding some small mapping exposure. Spring and the early summer are a better time before the vegetation has put on too much growth. Much can even be done during the late autumn and winter. The days may be short, but the vegetation is dying or has died down, so one can be certain that one has worked thoroughly over a piece of ground in considerably less time than in the summer. One cannot map, however, when the ground is snow covered or frozen or too sodden after prolonged rainfall or thaw. Spring lines may also be more difficult to detect in the high summer when the ground is baked and the discharge of the springs failing. Anyone who lives near to the area that he is mapping is fortunate, for he can visit and revisit it, particularly the more difficult parts, at different seasons and study the ground under differing moisture contents. Similarly, if one is mapping a coastal area, one must take every advantage of abnormally low tides that may uncover outcrops that are usually hidden.

Tracing the top of a feature-forming bed, that is the limit of its dip slope, is often more difficult than mapping its base along the foot of its scarp. The change in the form of the ground is less pronounced and hence more difficult to detect, but on the other hand, there is less likelihood of thick downwash, so augering may be more effective.

One must record either on the field map or in the notebook or using the two in combination, the nature of the evidence, exposure, soil change, spring line, feature, etc. by which each boundary has been traced.

Mapping the base and the top of the feature-forming beds will automatically delimit the outcrops of the softer beds in the succession. But one must also traverse thoroughly all the ground between these boundaries. There may be minor units that can be followed either along the scarps or the parts of the dip slopes, especially where these are not truly parallel to the dip of the rocks, but cut across them at a slight angle. As will be seen later (p. 38) one needs as much evidence as possible when mapping faults and other structural features. Also one should map not only the solid rocks but also any drift deposits that may be present.

Mapping Drift Deposits

Some features formed by drift deposits, such as morainic ridges, drumlins, the alluvial fill along the valley of a river or the terraces bordering the river, or coastal sand dunes, are easily recognizable and have sharply defined margins. Elsewhere the drift cover may not give rise to such distinctive topography. The older the drift deposit, the greater the amount of time that it has been affected by weathering with gradual loss of its original form by the slow effects of soil creep and other forms of downwash. The beautifully clear examples of moraines, long stretches of raised beach, glacial lake features, etc., illustrated in so many text-books, are all of very recent origin geologically speaking, their age being measurable only in thousands of years.

Drift deposits of glacial origin usually contain rocks and pebbles ('erratics') that have been brought from a distance and are markedly different from the local material. In between exposures, such erratics should be looked for in farm tracks, on the fields (especially after ploughing), in the soil of gardens, in the material thrown up from ditches, etc. By recording on the map whereever such distinctive erratics have been found one gradually delimits the extent of the deposits containing them. Drift mapping of this type is time consuming, for not only must one cover the ground thoroughly, but one must also consider the possibility of human activity, e.g. a small patch of gravel may have been brought there to mend a muddy place in a farm track and then spread onto the fields by the plough.

More difficult to delimit are the spreads of Head, composed of local material that has sludged down often quite gentle slopes under periglacial (freeze–thaw) conditions. Such deposits may be readily enough recognized in an exposure (No. 16), but in between the exposures one has to look for such evidence as the presence in the soil of numerous blocks or small fragments, usually markedly angular, of local hard rocks well below their mapped outcrop. The extent of the spreads of calcareous Head (Coombe Rock) across the outcrops of the sands and clays outcropping at the foot of the great scarps formed by the Chalk and other limestones can be traced by noting the presence or absence of that very distinctive lime-loving plant *Clematis vitalba* (Traveller's Joy or Old Man's Beard). But plants as indicators of soil characters must always be treated with reserve by the geological mapper, for there is the ever-present possibility of human planting with perhaps alteration of the soil. Residual deposits – Clay with Flints, terra rossa, etc. – may also mantle the dip slope of the thicker limestones. The base and therefore the thickness of such deposits will be markedly irregular, owing to the effects of solution of the underlying calcareous rocks (Nos. 3, 47). Sludging will also have occurred down the sides of the valleys worn into the limestone cuesta. Mapping the limits of such deposits is only too often a slow and difficult process. One can decide to work to some arbitrary limit, such as the thickness must be greater than one metre, but how does one keep to this where there are no exposures? Augering may be no easy matter into Clay with Flints or stony Head. The beginner would be well advised to avoid areas where Head and Clay with Flints are extensively developed. The other types of drift deposit – alluvium, river terraces, sand dunes, even boulder clay and outwash gravels, are usually much easier to delimit.

Superficial Structures

The periglacial conditions that occurred to the south of the fluctuating ice sheets of the Pleistocene produced not only Head, but also, locally, mass movement and disruption of thick beds of the more competent sedimentary rocks. Deep road cuts through scarps have shown that near the crest of the scarp, the beds may be broken into blocks by deep fractures with many of the blocks dipping down the scarp face, suggesting that an anticline runs along the crest of the scarp (Fig. 5). When tracing the base of a competent bed (limestone, sandstone or ironstone) overlying clays along the face of a scarp or round the deeper cut valleys of the dip slope, one may find that the boundary has moved downhill for a distance and then returned to its former level. If the beds are exposed in a quarry, they will be found not only to be dipping downhill, but to be cut by closely spaced faults. The throw of each fault may be small, often measurable in centimetres rather than metres, but the aggregate effect of this step faulting is considerable. In places, a pair of larger faults, throwing towards each other, may have dropped down a narrow strip of beds higher in the succession than those exposed elsewhere in the quarry. These beds may not be workable, so the quarrymen have left these 'gulls', to use their term, as upstanding blocks across the workings. Sometimes gulls may contain boulder clay, which has been stripped off from the rocks on either side. Such gulls can be traced across the fields on either side of the quarry by a scattered line of erratics.

Cambering is the name given to such a mass movement of beds as a result of past periglacial conditions. On their more recent maps the Geological Survey use special symbols to show the extent both of land-slipped and of cambered ground. Any major constructional work, including trunk roads, on such disturbed ground, will clearly be hazardous.

Upward bulging of the incompetent clays in the valley bottoms may also occur where they were unable to sustain the pressure of the overlying competent beds. This will produce anticlinal, sometimes faulted, structures with quite steep outward dips, but borings show that such *valley bulges* die out rapidly downwards. Also the trend of their axes follows not the strike of the beds, but the line of the valleys. The structures associated with cambering are therefore only superficial as compared with the deeper seated structures of tectonic origin. If they should occur on one's mapping area, they must be mapped in the normal way.

Superficial structures must not be confused with *soil creep*, the slow movement of rock material downhill under gravity. Soil creep can affect all types of rocks, sedimentary, igneous or metamorphic, but superficial structures only occur in areas of gently dipping sedimentary rocks. It is most important not to be misled by the effects of soil creep when taking dip readings. The lines of tabular rock fragments may be inclined at a totally different direction from the true dip of the beds (No. 153).

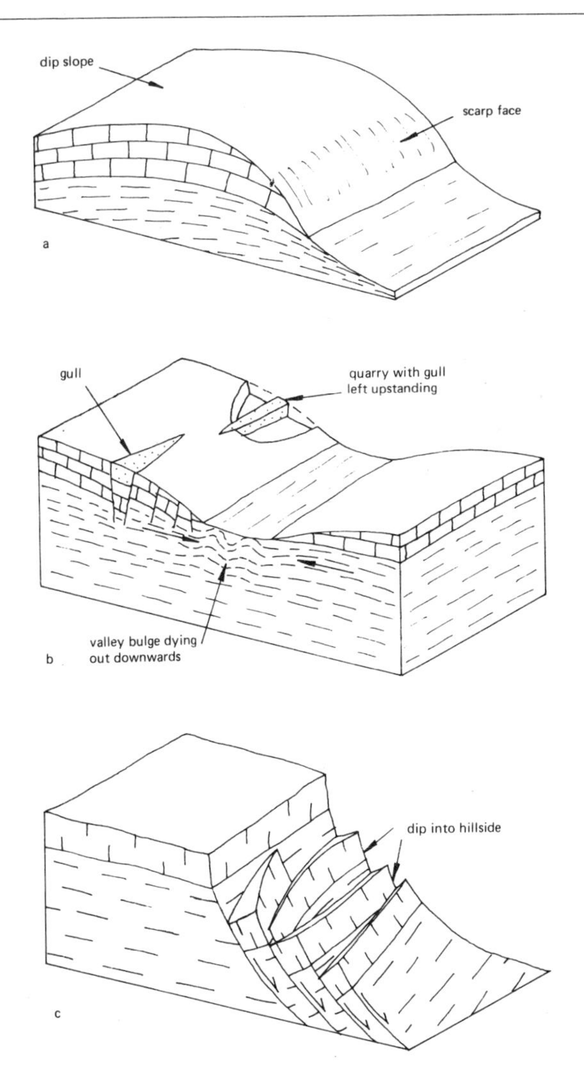

Fig. 5. a *Camber*. b *Valley bulging and development of gulls*. c *Landslipping along curved slide planes*.

Mapping Faults

In an exposure the presence of a fault is shown by the abrupt displacement of rocks along a plane that is usually steeply inclined (No. 88). Along the fault plane there is often a narrow zone of broken and brecciated rocks and this zone may also be mineralized. The strike of the fault can be marked on the map and evidence for faulting sought along the extension of this line. A distinctive bed, traceable by outcrop evidence, by features, etc., will end abruptly where it is cut off by a fault. The shattered rocks along the fault may have been etched out to form a strip of low ground or a col in a ridge. Faulting may have thrown a permeable bed against impermeable rocks, so that there is seepage and perhaps springs along the suspected line of the fault. If the fault has been mineralized, its continuation may be marked by a line of old mine workings or trial holes (No. 156).

These are the lines of evidence to be looked for when tracing a known fault, particularly one whose trend is perpendicular or oblique to the strike of the beds and whose throw is sufficient to displace (offset) the outcrop. It is a more difficult matter when the fault plane is not clearly exposed and the presence of the fault can only be inferred. The termination of a mappable horizon, which one has been confidently following for some distance, may well be due to faulting, but one must search for confirmatory evidence. Failure to trace a bed may be due to a rather rapid change in its lithology, to its disappearance under a cover of drift or to a number of other possibilities. If, however, the outcrops of several of the over- and under-lying beds also end abruptly on the same line this is much more suggestive of faulting, for it is unlikely that channelling or some other depositional feature would affect a thickness of beds along a definite line, whilst the margins of drift deposits are usually sinuous. Is there any evidence of seepage along the suspected fault line? A more careful examination may detect fragments of brecciated or mineralized rock. Faults should not be shown on the map unless the actual fault plane has been found or the mapped outcrop pattern cannot be explained in any other way. The beginner in geological mapping is far too apt to insert faults on insufficient evidence.

This is particularly the case with inferred (unexposed) strike faults. The width of the outcrop of a bed is a function of its dip, its thickness and the form of the ground – almost flat, sloping with or sloping against the dip. The construction of block diagrams or sections, showing how the width of outcrop of a bed may be reduced by a normal strike fault throwing against the dip or increased when such a fault throws with the dip, is a familiar classroom exercise. But similar effects on the width of outcrop may be produced by just a local steepening or flattening of the dip. If one knows the approximate thickness of the beds one is mapping, it is a useful exercise to draw scale sections across suspected strike faults to check if the marked widening or narrowing of the outcrop could not be due to a local change of dip rather than to strike faulting. If the outcrop of the bed is not wide enough to accommodate the whole thickness of the bed (it would then be vertical), the case for faulting is greatly strengthened, especially if parts of the succession, recognizable elsewhere, cannot be found along the line of the inferred fault.

Fault planes of low dip and gently dipping thrust planes naturally have very much more sinuous outcrops than steeply inclined faults. One can trace them by the same methods, though if there is little difference between the rocks occurring above and below the thrust plane this may be no easy matter. Where markedly different rocks are brought into contact, for example the schists above and limestones beneath the Moine Thrust at and behind Knockan in the N.W. Highlands of Scotland, the outcrop of the thrust plane is easily recognizable from the very different types of country on either side of it. Beneath a major thrust or between two major thrusts, closely spaced high-angle thrusts may be developed to produce a belt of imbrication (Fig. 6).

If strongly contrasting rock-types are involved, such as the distinctive quartzites, the Pipe Rock (No. 21) and the limestones in the neighbourhood of Loch Assynt, Sutherlandshire, along parts of the great thrusts of the N.W. Highlands, then the details of such imbricate zones can be worked out on the ground fairly easily, but if the beds affected are of more uniform lithology then the task of the geological mapper is much more difficult.

It is the same along the line of major faults, such as those on either side of the Great Glen in Scotland or the Rhine Rift in Germany. The general line of the faults is readily apparent, owing to the marked difference in relief between the upthrown and the downthrown blocks. The fault-line scarps are indeed impressive, but their lower parts are mantled by downwash and in the case of the Great Glen plastered over with glacial drift, so that the exact position of the major faults and of any subsidiary faults is often very difficult to determine on the ground.

Mapping on Hard-rocks

These areas are usually of much greater and more varied relief than the scarpland topography developed on the more gently dipping younger beds. One must concentrate on the exposures formed by the small crags and other outcrops where the beds stand out above the cover of grass or other vegetation or where they can be seen in the sides and bottoms of the streams flowing down the steep hill sides. Quarries are likely to be fewer, though road cuts may provide

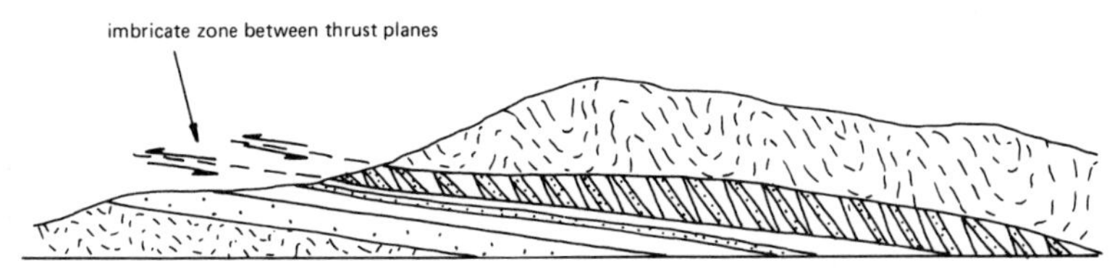

Fig. 6. *Thrust zone with imbricate structure.*

valuable sections. It is usually far more difficult to find evidence in between such exposures, for augering is impracticable, soil changes are less marked than on the softer rocks, helpful burrowing animals are less common and features are usually more difficult to recognize and trace. Great spreads of peat may swathe the broad upland ridges, whilst boulder clay and other drift deposits may be extensively developed along the valleys.

If one is mapping on the scale of 1 : 10,000 or greater, it is usually possible to record on the map the positions of all the outcrops, unless they are very close together, with the nature of the beds, their dip and direction of strike, cleavage and other structural features. As already mentioned (p. 28), vertical aerial photographs are often of great help in mapping such areas. If a junction is exposed or if two adjacent crags expose different rocks, then a firm boundary can be drawn. If the two exposures are too far apart, then a dotted line must be placed between them. In this way the boundaries can be traced, with varying degrees of certainty, through the scattered outcrops. The softer the rock-type – the more argillaceous or pelitic it is – the less likely for it to outcrop, even in the stream sections, so the location of belts of poorly exposed ground is suggestive. The base of a harder band – a more arenaceous (psammitic) sedimentary or metasedimentary or igneous rock – may well be marked by a feature capped by a line of rocky outcrops. One must seek evidence to show where precisely to draw the boundary along the face of the feature. The difficulty is to be certain whether the blocks that protrude through the turf along the lower part of the feature are really *in situ*. They may have fallen from the crags above, rolled or slid down the slope and then the turf has grown around them. If such blocks show markedly different dips and strikes from those measurable on the crags above they are probably not in place. One can stand on the block and tap it with a hammer. If the vibrations felt by one's feet are marked, and the hammer blow sounds of low pitch, the boulder is not *in situ*, but is embedded in the soil or drift. Conversely faint vibrations and a higher pitched noise mean that it is either part of the solid rock or is a very large detached block.

As one's eye becomes accustomed to the area, one begins to recognize the different rock types from a distance with increasing certainty. One can distinguish slight differences in colour or in the manner in which the different rocks weather. But such impressions must always be checked by inspection of rock surfaces. Lichen or other growths can be highly misleading, so if necessary, use the hammer to expose a clean surface.

The Importance of Small Scale Structures

The geological structures encountered in hard rock areas are much more complex than those in soft rock, and it is therefore in the observation and interpretation of these structures that the mapping techniques differ. Fault planes can be traced as described above (p. 38), just as they can in soft rock country, but there are likely to be more of them, often cross-cutting one another (e.g. a gently dipping thrust cut by later normal faults). *Strike faults*, those which strike parallel to the strike of the strata, often with a similar dip as well, can be especially difficult, or even impossible, to detect.

The most important technique in hard rock mapping is the use of minor (small scale) structures to indicate the nature and attitude of the major structures. In areas which have been at least strongly folded and faulted, with dips commonly greater than 20–30°, minor folding tends to become ubiquitous, particularly where the rocks are well laminated, and it can be observed in outcrop (e.g. Nos 139–142). From these minor structures we can infer both the attitude of the major structures, and the sequence of structural events. In effect the major structures are examined in microcosm, in the scale models provided by the minor folds (and faults) in outcrop. A single exposure could conceivably yield sufficient information to determine the fold type and attitude (or orientation) of the major folds in the area, including the refolding of the earlier folds. Additionally the small minor faults (or *shears* as they are often called) could be observed cutting each other and the folds, giving a clue to the strike and dip, and the sense of movement, of major faults. Infilled veins, joints and tension joints, can all also be added to the story read from one outcrop. Where the crystallization of metamorphic minerals can be related to the sequence of events, the story can be further elaborated. However, this is mainly a matter for microscope study, though the growth of large crystals may be worked out in the field.

In mapping a complex area one may expect to find a partial story of this type for each exposure, and this 'model' of the events will be continually checked, modified and expanded as mapping proceeds. Firstly, a gradually more accurate and complete sequence of events will emerge, with later events cutting or deforming the earlier. Secondly, the dip and strike of planar structures, and the attitude of linear structures may vary systematically from outcrop to outcrop, and mapping of these variations will yield further information. A structural map or several maps can be drawn, to complement the stratigraphic map, which will normally show the distribution of rock types, and the 'mappable' faults (those which will show a displacement when plotted on the scale of the field map).

Folding and Cleavage or Foliation

A slaty cleavage or a foliation or schistosity is often (though not always) parallel to the axial planes of those folds which formed at the same time (p. 69). Evidence for this should be looked for when mapping, for example when examining fold hinges (Fig. 7 and No. 139). If this relationship does hold, the strike and dip of the cleavage can then be used as a measure of the strike and dip of the axial planes of the folds, and any variations in fold trends will be indicated by a swing in the cleavage. Where they are not parallel, bedding and cleavage planes will intersect in a series of lines parallel to one another and to the axis of the fold. In many outcrops the trend and plunge of this line can be observed and measured, and plotted on a map to show the plunge of the folds: the arrows will diverge from plunge culminations and converge on plunge depressions.

Figure 7 shows an anticline and a syncline, with associated minor folds and an axial plane cleavage. If small exposures are examined, such as those in the insets, the bedding/cleavage relationship within them can be used to determine their position with reference to the major folds. Both the angular relationship between the bedding and the cleavage, and the small fold pairs are used here, the syncline of a fold pair being nearer to the major anticline. Sedimentary evidence for 'way-up' or 'younging' (e.g. graded bedding, ripple marks, cross bedding, etc.) should always be looked for in mapping, and used as an aid in interpretation of the structure. In Fig. 8a the beds 'young' away from the core of the anticline, and towards the core of the syncline, which is the situation in areas which have been simply tightly folded. The beds become younger as we trace them up the axial plane of a fold, though they may be overturned

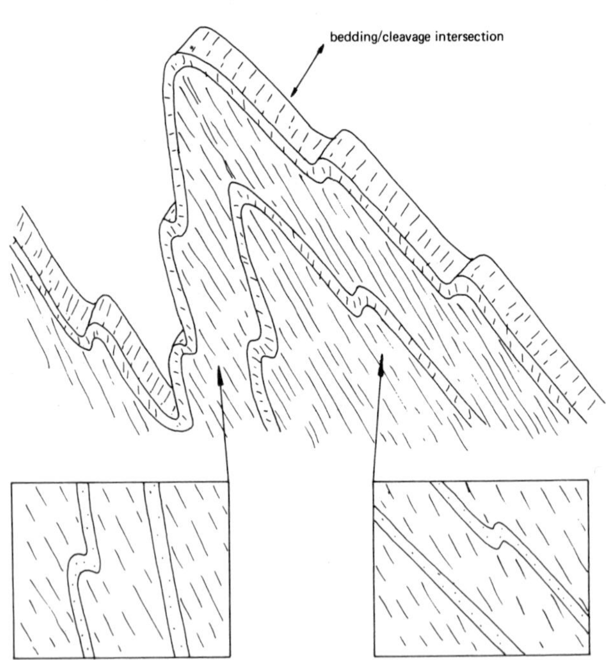

Fig. 7. *The relation between bedding and cleavage in folded strata. The insets show the likely appearance of outcrops on the fold limbs (cf. Nos 78, 79, 82).*

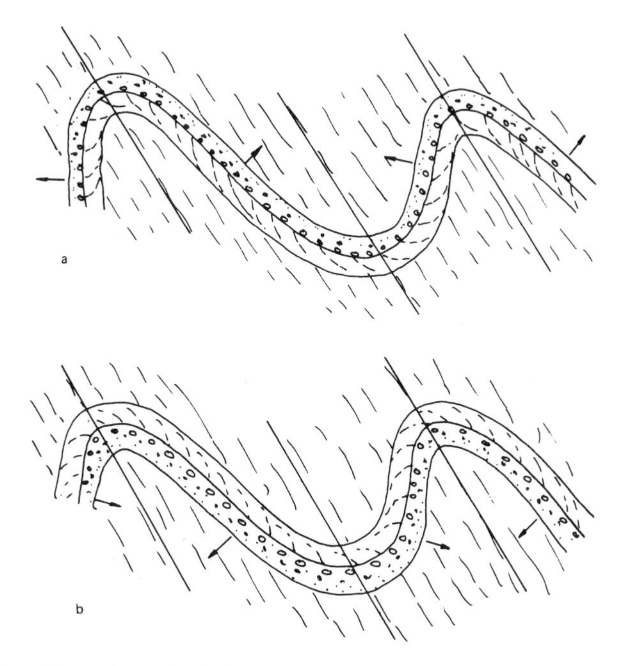

Fig. 8. a *Upward facing folds.* b *Downward facing folds. Arrows indicate the direction of 'younging'.*

on a fold limb where they have been rotated through the vertical. However, if we are dealing with a complexly folded and faulted region, the beds may be observed in some localities to become younger down the axial planes, the converse of the normal situation (Fig. 8b). Such structures are said to be *downward facing*, and in this situation (or when the direction of facing is not known), the upfolds are termed *antiforms*, and the downfolds *synforms* (No. 74).

Downward facing structures of this type are principally found in folded belts where recumbent folds and thrusts result in large scale horizontal movement. In the nose and lower part of the fold which results (a *nappe*) the structures will be downwards facing. The sketch cross-section of the Tay Nappe in Scotland (Fig. 9) shows that these structures can be many miles in amplitude, and mapping on a regional scale is necessary to prove them. Within a small map area all the major folds may be downward facing, horizontal or sideways facing, or upward facing, depending where the area is with relation to the major nappe. These three regions are respectively in the

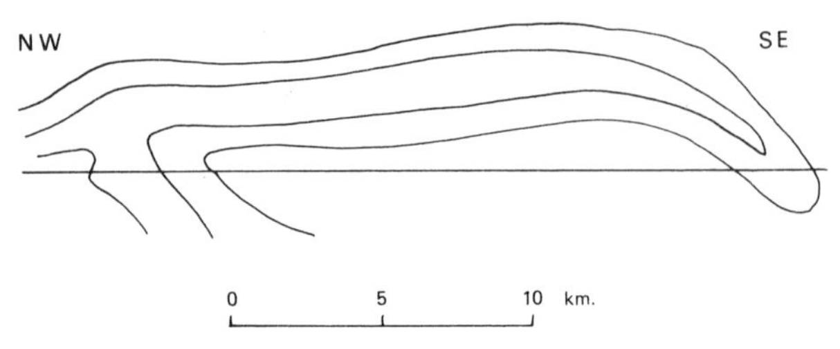

Fig. 9. *Cross section of the Tay Nappe.*

nose, the flat belt and the root zone of the nappe.

If a region has been folded more than once, on axial planes which may differ in their orientation, the resultant pattern of outcrops due to the interference of these folds may be quite complex, producing, even on a flattish topography, hook (No. 142), eye (No. 144) or more complex structures, accompanied by variations in the direction of strike, in contrast to the linear patterns produced in one phase of strong folding. This type of complexity is characteristic of many metamorphic regions, and demands considerable experience and ability to think and visualize in three dimensions to unravel. Two examples of these types of structures are illustrated (Nos 142, 144) on an outcrop scale: yet another case of the minor structures leading to interpretation of the major structures. Associated with these structures there may be the development of a new schistosity, obliterating the older original one, a process which can eventually lead to loss of all the earlier structures, both sedimentary and tectonic.

Veins and Joints

The strike and dip of these structures should be measured, together with the trend and plunge of any mineral fibres. Details of the mineral infilling, including the relative order of crystallization of the different minerals within a vein, and of different veins must also be recorded. Crystals with idiomorphic habit (i.e. their crystal shapes have developed without interlocking) were precipitated within a cavity, indicating that the walls of the vein had moved apart.

The relative chronology derived from cross-cutting relationships (e.g. No. 100) will of course be added to the sequence of deformation events. As with bedding and foliation, their distribution and attitude can be plotted, either on a diagram or on a map. A rose diagram (Fig. 10) can be used for near vertical structures, where it is evident that the pattern does not vary in orientation over the area being studied. If the structures are not vertical, they may have to be plotted on a stereographic projection, a more complex graphical device which will show both the strike and dip of the structures.

A map or maps of the structures will show variation in their attitude over a region, and can make these variations more obvious than simply looking at notebook records. Joints may change their orientation across

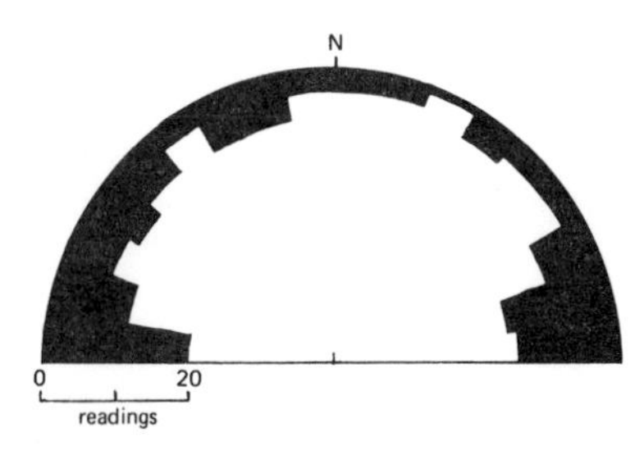

Fig. 10. *Rose diagram of near vertical joints in the area of the sample field map.*

the axis of a fold (Fig. 11), or they may trend parallel to the margin of an intrusion. Veins bearing metallic minerals may have a different trend to barren ones. Small scale faults with slickensides or striated surfaces may be parallel to and concentrated near the line of a postulated fault, and mineral infilled veins may be similarly concentrated.

Writing the Report

The observations recorded on the field maps or in the field notebooks should finally be welded together into a report setting out clearly the geological features of the area and its geological history. The results of any subsequent examination in the laboratory of the rocks, minerals and fossils collected should be incorporated in the report. The report should be illustrated by maps, sections and any other diagrams necessary to bring out clearly the structure and other features of the area. Also one should comment on any localities where the mapping evidence could be interpreted in more than one way, discussing the various possibilities and stating the reasons for favouring one particular interpretation. Poorly exposed ground may well be difficult to analyse and interpret.

A possible framework for such a report would be for it to commence with the location of the area in terms of its geological setting and the succession of beds present. Then a concise description of the topography, stressing those units which have a distinctive topographic expression, those which are poorly exposed and any significant features of the drift deposits. It might also be appropriate to mention here any

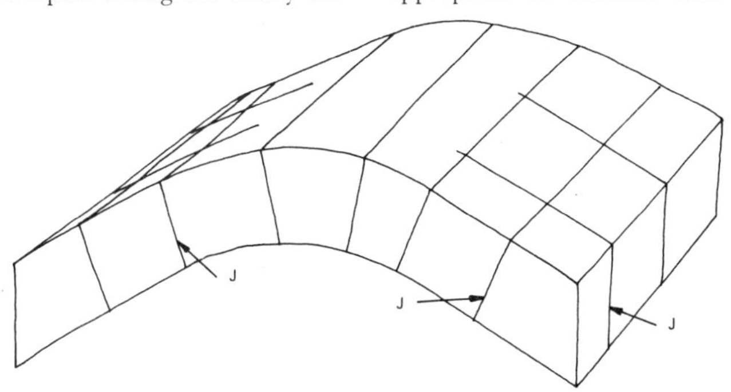

Fig. 11. *Diagrammatic fold, with associated joint planes (J).*

places where the location of the boundaries was particularly difficult. Having thus given the background to the area and also some indication of the reliability of the mapping, one can then proceed to describe the succession in detail, working from the oldest to the youngest bed. If there is a limit to the length of the report, much of the stratigraphical detail can be condensed into a columnar section, showing the thickness, lithology, fauna and other features of each unit. In the text one can then concentrate on any lateral or vertical variations noted. One can then deal with the structure of the area, describing each structural event in chronological order. Sections, diagrams, etc., are again preferable to too much unillustrated text. If a major unconformity is present, it will be preferable to separate both the stratigraphical and structural history into pre-unconformity and post-unconformity sections. Extrusive igneous rocks will be dealt with at the appropriate stratigraphical level and any intrusive igneous rocks, mineralization or metamorphism at their place or places in the history of the area. Finally, the drift deposits must be described. The report should conclude with a summary of the geological history of the area.

The journals of the main geological societies contain many accounts of the geology of specific areas, which can be used both as guides to the areas described, and as examples of field reports whose layout is worth studying. The Sheet and District Memoirs of the Institute of Geological Sciences use similar layouts and usually have the space to go into greater detail than can be given in a journal. Their Regional Handbooks follow the same layout, though having to state the geology in much more general terms and without referring in detail to individual exposures.

II ROCKS AND STRUCTURES TO BE OBSERVED IN THE FIELD

3 SEDIMENTARY ROCKS

The *sedimentary rocks* are those which have formed at the surface of the earth by surface processes (excluding the volcanic igneous rocks which have solidified from a molten magma). The term *sediment* brings to mind sand or mud settling out in water, but in geology it is used in a wider sense to include rocks derived by chemical and organic processes. It is used strictly to describe the material which has accumulated, before lithification to form the sedimentary rock, but it is often used to refer to the latter as well (e.g. sand is the sediment, and sandstone the sedimentary rock, but a sandstone is often described as a sediment).

Clastic (*detrital* or *mechanical*) sediments form the most important sedimentary rocks, by volume. The particles of sediment are carried and deposited as solid material, without the involvement of chemical processes. *Chemical deposits* involve solution and precipitation: they include many limestones, ironstones and evaporites. *Organic deposits* form a third category, including some limestones, peats and coals.

Although the sedimentary rocks can be divided into these three categories, there are gradations between them: a rock can be formed by a combination of all three processes. Often a clastic rock will have a matrix or cement which was deposited by precipitation, while an organic reef rock can have detrital material between the organic skeletons. Two types of terms are used to describe sedimentary rocks. Firstly, purely descriptive terms (e.g. sandstone, limestone) are more widely used, and do not imply a particular mode of deposition. Descriptive adjectives may be added to give more detail: sandy limestone, fine sandstone, sandy calcareous shale. Secondly, a genetic terminology implying a particular mode of origin is less easy to apply. An aeolian sandstone is deposited from wind-blown debris, and a turbidite from a density current which carried the particles in suspension. In recent years sedimentologists have greatly increased the number of such terms in use, but they are not easily applied in the field in many cases, and care should be taken in their use.

The relationships between sedimentary rocks are as important as the characteristics of individual rock units. These relations, both in space and in time, lead to the understanding of the history of the succession seen. One sediment may pass into another by gradation, or by an abrupt change. A succession of sedimentary rocks may show a gradual change in type, reflecting a progression from say a beach conglomerate to offshore mudstones, or a rhythmic repetition of beds, a *cyclothem*, such as those of the Coal Measures (Fig. 12). Gradually, a sequence of events will be built up for an area – a succession of palaeogeographies which will give the geological history. The superficial deposits, soils, alluvium, beach sediments and glacial deposits, will bring the story up to the present day, though there may be a large gap between them and the earlier solid rock, a large unconformity which indicates missing chapters in the story.

Clastic Rocks

Clastic rocks are formed from mechanically deposited aggregates of particles (*clasts*) ranging in size from clay (mudstones, shales) through silt (siltstones), sand and grit (sandstones and grits) to pebbles and boulders (conglomerates and breccias). The geological terms argillaceous (muddy), arenaceous (sandy) and rudaceous (pebbly) are commonly used as descriptive terms for the different grain sizes. Of course, as there are all variations possible between them, the terms are restricted to classes, with arbitrary divisions between them. Several different schemes for this exist, one frequently used being:

Conglomerates and breccias (rudaceous) 2mm upwards.
Grits and sandstones (arenaceous) 0.06mm–2mm
Mudstones and shales (argillaceous) less than 0.06mm (silt and clay)

These schemes reflect one important factor: the mudstones are composed principally of clay minerals, which fragment or cleave along the mineral cleavage to minute flaky particles, easily carried by water currents in suspension, or blown by wind. In the coarser rocks the grains are overwhelmingly of the stable mineral, quartz, which is granular in texture and does not cleave. Additionally, the coarser rocks have two components. The grains or pebbles form the bulk of the rock, and are referred to as the *framework*, while the spaces between contain a cementing material termed the *matrix*. This may be simply composed of finer sediment than the framework – sand, silt or mud (clay) – or may be a chemical precipitate from percolating pore water, postdating the accumulation of the original sediment.

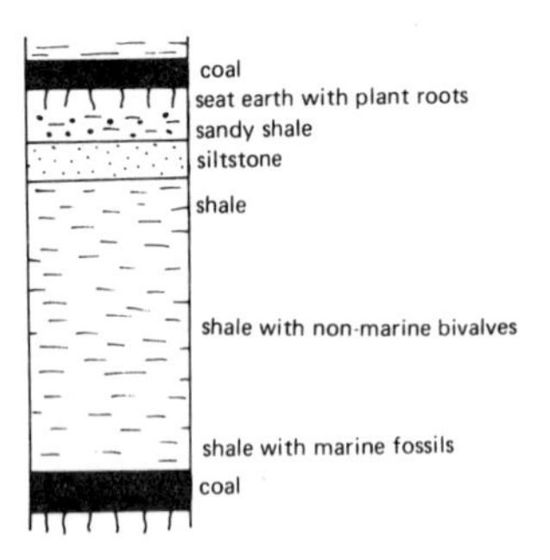

Fig. 12. *Vertical section through a Coal Measure cyclothem.*

Rudaceous Rocks

The large grain size of these implies in most cases either swift water currents to move the large pebbles (Nos 1, 5), or formation of the rock *in situ* (No. 3). The angularity of the framework is also significant, the angular blocks in a *breccia* signifying little transport of the blocks, either in time or in space. Conversely the rounded blocks in a *conglomerate* indicate a more mature sediment, which has undergone more attrition or wearing down of the pebbles. In these coarse rocks the individual pebbles are often of recognizable rock types, rather than individual mineral grains. Indeed boulders of conglomerate within a conglomerate are known.

Marine conglomerates are most commonly associated with beach deposits. They can be seen forming on pebble and boulder beaches (No. 52) and can be recognized in raised beach deposits (No. 10). In these environments they rest unconformably on the rocks being eroded to form the beach, and similar conditions probably obtained during the formation of basal conglomerates (No. 4).

Conglomerates and breccias are also found with a muddy matrix, interbedded with shales or mudstones, in situations which preclude an immediate shallow water or fluviatile origin. These features, together with other evidence, suggest that some of these deposits may have slid *en masse* down a submarine slope into their present position. Mud in suspension (as in a turbidity current) may have helped to move the larger blocks, and slide conglomerates of this type can grade laterally into turbidites.

Terrestrial conglomerates and breccias, formed without water action, are the scree deposits and breccias, infrequently found in fossil form, but easily observed at the present day land surface. Like marine beach deposits, they often rest unconformably on the surface of older rocks, and the pebbles are both very angular and locally derived (No. 3).

Fresh water conglomerates can be seen forming in rivers, as gravel and boulder accumulations perhaps only moved in times of flood. Interbedding of the conglomerate with water deposited sands may indicate this fluvial origin (No. 1), together with a red colour (due to iron oxides) of the type found in both the Old and New Red Sandstones. Some of the conglomerates of the Old Red Sandstone are spectacular, both in boulder size and in thickness of strata, suggesting landscapes and processes on a grand scale.

Ill-graded Deposits of Glacial Origin

Glacial conglomerates and gravels are transported and deposited from running meltwater, either close to the ice margin or within or on the ice. The former are outwash deposits, laid down in streams and temporary lakes. They are laterally and vertically very variable; conglomerates may be interbedded with sandstones or may form lenses as the meltwater streams changed their courses. Similar deposits form in or on the ice, but as the ice melts and disappears these deposits may collapse and their internal bedding will be disturbed. A subglacial or englacial stream will leave a ribbon or embankment of material meandering across country (an *esker*). In recently glaciated regions, like Ireland and Scandinavia, these eskers form dry lines of communication across otherwise swampy ground, and may also be worked as gravel and sand deposits. The boulders found in these deposits have come from the regions traversed by the ice, which may have been of continental extent. They may show striations on their surfaces, and an occasional pebble may have been ground flat on one side.

Material deposited *in situ* by the wasting or melting of an ice mass (*boulder clay*) differs markedly from glacio-fluvial deposits: particles of all sizes are left behind in an unstratified deposit. The finest material, rock flour, formed by the grinding action of the ice, forms the matrix, while sand, gravel and boulders carried by the ice are randomly scattered within it. Boulder clay (No. 12) forms the principal sediment left by the great Pleistocene ice sheets, spread thickly over the lower ground.

The outwash deposits are found near the margin of the ice sheets, and also sporadically over the boulder clay, especially where still-stands occurred during the retreat of the ice. Subsequent re-advance of the ice sheet may result in another spread of boulder clay over the earlier deposits, giving a sequence of boulder clay, outwash deposits and boulder clay. Such a sequence has been interpreted in many places as representing two glaciations, though there is no guarantee that this is so. During melting of an ice sheet, boulder clay may be interleaved with glacio-fluvial deposits: englacial river deposits can be sandwiched between two boulder clays, the whole sequence being deposited during a continuous retreat of one ice sheet.

In glacial deposits, as with all sediments, the transported boulders and pebbles (*erratic blocks* or *erratics*) may furnish valuable information on the provenance, or source of the ice, and its route. The more distinct or unusual rock types, particularly those whose area of outcrop is distinctly limited in size, will be of more use than those which are common or not easily distinguishable. The distinctive microgranite of Ailsa Craig, a small island in the Clyde estuary of Scotland, is easily recognized, and forms a marker erratic in the boulder clays in Ireland, England and north Wales. The drifts in east Anglia contain boulders derived from ice which moved across the North Sea from Scandinavia.

The most easily recognized and widespread glacial deposits are those of the Pleistocene ice sheets, which form widespread superficial deposits in northern Europe, northern N. America, and in the southern hemisphere in New Zealand and elsewhere. Older sequences of glacial deposits are less well known, and more difficult to identify, but are of considerable interest. Fossil boulder clays and other glacial deposits have been identified from the late Pre-Cambrian, the Ordovician and the Permo–Carboniferous. Some of these fossil boulder clays, termed *tillites*, were dropped from floating ice in marine sequences, and it is difficult to separate them from slide conglomerates or breccias, though striated boulders are a good indicator. In some areas the deposits occur in terrestrial sequences, in which a wider variety of sediments and features, including striated surfaces, can be found (No. 15).

In the regions of permafrost, such as Alaska and northern Siberia, with the ground frozen at depth but without a permanent ice cover, the surface layers, subjected to annual freezing and thawing, develop distinctive features and deposits. Exposed rock surfaces are shattered by frost action. On even gentle slopes the surface layers thaw out, and as their contained water cannot drain downwards owing to the permanently frozen layers at depth, the soil and rock debris flows downhill to produce *solifluction* or *periglacial* deposits. *Head* is the name given to such deposits formed during the geological past (p. 35). The rock fragments tend to lie either parallel to the surface of the ground or are rotated with their longest axis vertical. Where easy flowage is impeded the periglacial deposits may become convoluted or folded (No. 14). Comparable folding can also be developed in the more viscous parts of the ice sheets to produce the spectacular over-folds and thrusts of the 'Contorted Drift' of the north Norfolk coast or of the 'push moraines' of north Germany and elsewhere (No. 17). On more level ground frost or ice wedges may occur, somewhat analogous to mudcracks in dried sediment. They show up in sections as near vertical zones of disturbed material, sometimes different in colour from the rest of the deposit (No. 13).

Residual Deposits

These are formed by the breakup of rocks under chemical weathering without appreciable lateral transportation. The Chalk cuestas are mantled with *Clay with Flints* consisting of all sizes of flints ranging in shape from angular to well rounded in a matrix of reddish clay and sand. They are the insoluble material left behind by the solution of the Chalk and its covering of flint pebble beds, sands and clays of Tertiary age. Clay with Flints often shows signs of disturbance due to past periglacial conditions. Under the intense chemical weathering of the more humid tropical regions, a variety of sedimentary, igneous and metamorphic rocks break down to form the iron-rich *laterites* and the more alumina-rich *bauxites*. Fossil soils of this type, sometimes referred to as 'bole', can be seen at the Giant's Causeway in Antrim (Nos 116, 117). *Terra rossa* is a red soil rich in iron hydroxides, formed from the weathering of limestones.

Arenaceous Rocks

Sandstones are found as important constituents of many successions, generally in near shore, fresh water, or aeolian (wind blown) environments.

Aeolian sandstones are marked by very even-sized grains, generally almost spherical and with a matt surface. The bedding planes reflect the sand dunes whose accumulation makes up the sandstones. The bedding in individual units dips up to the angle of repose of the sand, and the thickness of the units, up to several metres, reflects the size of the dunes. The matrix often represents a subsequent chemical precipitation of material. Coastal sand dunes, such as those found round the coasts of Britain, are unlikely to be preserved in the geological record. They contain shell fragments, and should be associated with marine sediments. Desert sands, however, are found in the geological record associated with other terrestrial sediments, and can be both thick and widespread (No. 19).

Water-lain sandstones, either marine or fresh water, show a much greater variety of both constituent grains and of sedimentary structures. Grain shape, as with conglomerates, varies with the maturity of the rock – the length of time during which the grains have been transported and abraded. The evenness of grain size (the *degree of sorting*) is also much more variable than in aeolian sandstones, though it rarely reaches the variableness seen in turbidites.

Sandstones rarely show even, parallel bedding planes for more than a few centimetres. Instead, current bedding, and small scale erosion surfaces, are ubiquitous. Current bedding, representing at its simplest the deposition of foreset beds on minute delta fronts a few centimetres high, indicates sediment being built out laterally instead of vertically. Current fluctuations in shallow water environments often result in the erosion of sediment, with the succeeding sediment resting on the earlier with a minute unconformity. Such breaks, which do not in most cases represent a withdrawal of the sea, are called *erosion surfaces* (No. 1). They may occur where a river changes its bed, or major channel, where storm creates floods or increased wave action, or by tidal scour. Many of these situations can be examined in modern estuaries and beaches, and in rivers and lakes.

It is more difficult to study deeper water sandstones in course of deposition, and correspondingly less is known about them. In general one can say that they will be finer grained, erosion surfaces will be less common, and current directions will be more constant.

The matrix of many of these sandstones is a chemical one, though some interstitial mud may be present. Precipitation from pore water of iron oxide, lime or silica will result in ferruginous, calcareous or siliceous cements. Many freshwater sandstones have ferruginous cements: the New Red Sandstones have hematitic iron cements, while the rusty weathering of the Carboniferous Millstone Grit is due to limonite or siderite, the iron carbonate. Calcareous cements are common in sequences where sandstones are interbedded with limestones. Siliceous cements are interesting in that the silica is often deposited in optical continuity with the quartz grains, and the end result can be quartzite, with interlocking grains.

Arkoses are sandstones in which feldspars make up more than about 15% of the grains. Feldspar grains are physically and chemically less stable than quartz, but can be found in sandstones derived from igneous rocks, where the period of weathering and transport was short. More commonly the feldspars break down chemically to give clay minerals, to be carried in suspension and be deposited as clays and muds.

The finest grades of sand (0.6–0.004mm) are conveniently and commonly separated as *silt*, giving on induration a *siltstone*. Particles even of this size are predominantly of quartz, and will tend to be equidimensional, in contrast to the smaller and flaky clay minerals, and will behave differently in water. They can just be seen as separated grains using a handlens. If a piece of unconsolidated silt or clay containing silt is put between one's teeth, it will feel slightly gritty, whilst the rock may appear lighter in colour than the associated mudstones or shales.

Argillaceous Rocks

These are rocks composed of the flaky clay minerals, complex aluminium silicates which, like mica, cleave very easily into minute flakes. They are carried in water mainly in suspension, and this separates them from the coarser clastic materials (except in rocks like turbidites). They settle in very quiet water conditions, but can still accumulate in a variety of situations: in lakes, lagoons, tidal marshes, in relatively shallow seas where circulation is restricted, and on deep ocean floors.

The terms *mud* and *clay* are largely synonymous, and are usually used to refer to the unconsolidated deposit, which generally contains a high water content. If, with compaction and burial, the water content is gradually reduced, but the sediment is not lithified to a hard rock, it is still referred to as a clay (e.g. the Oxford Clay). Further hardening and loss of water will produce a *shale* if the flakes are aligned parallel to one another, or a *mudstone* if there is no strong preferred orientation of minerals. A shale will therefore split easily into parallel-sided pieces, while a mudstone will have a more blocky fracture. A *slate* is produced when the clay minerals are rotated out of their original position by tectonic forces, or new minerals are formed, their parallelism producing *slaty* cleavage (p. 69). In some slates, however, the slaty cleavage is still parallel to the bedding planes, and its presence may be difficult to detect within a small outcrop. Further, even where the cleavage is not parallel to the bedding planes, it may have obliterated the bedding, giving a rock with a single planar structure which could be either bedding or cleavage. In this case, only differences in lithology (No. 73), colour banding, or bands of fossils may be found, if searched for.

Argillaceous rocks are often rich in fossils: the quiet conditions of deposition ensure that there is little breakup or abrasion before burial, and the poor circulation of pore water often prevents any solution of shells. Most shells with chambers are crushed (No. 32) if the chambers were only filled with water during compaction, though sometimes they may have been filled with crystalline quartz or calcite which has then strengthened them. Concretions (p. 61) are common features of many argillaceous rocks, and may contain uncrushed fossils. Sometimes crushed specimens of the same fossils may be obtained from the surrounding rock, demonstrating that the concretions grew before compaction was severe enough to crush the shells.

Pre-lithification Deformation

Movement after deposition of sediment, when still wet and virtually still 'on' the sea floor, due to gravity or current drag, is described as *slumping*. When sediments are deposited on a slope, they may become unstable, and move sideways, with complex folding or balling up of the material, to give what is described as a directional slump. The geometry of the slump can be used to deduce the direction of movement, and hence the trend of the slope. Similar directional slumping can be caused by current drag; it is common in turbidites (No. 40).

Non-directional slump structures occur when a density inversion is present, the denser material lying over the less dense. This is an inherently unstable situation, and a trigger such as an earthquake shock or a storm may cause the underlying material to well up in a series of mushroom-shaped structures (*diapirs*) folding the upper layers and eventually punching through them (No. 42). No directional sense may be present in this case, though a good exposure, in three dimensions, may be necessary to determine this.

Slump structures can be present on all scales, from beds a few centimetres thick, up to tens of metres. Similarly the grain size of the sediment which has slumped can vary from mud up to extremely coarse conglomerate. Indeed some conglomerates, interbedded with shales and mudstones, are thought to have slid *en masse* down submarine slopes to their present position (p. 49). Analysis of all these sediments, in terms of their grain size and type, and of the direction of slumping, is important in relation to the palaeogeography of the basin in which they occur. They can also be used, in highly folded rocks, as a 'way-up' criterion, in interpreting both the folding and the succession. In examining such deformation attention should be paid to its vertical extent (whether it deforms one or several beds), upper surface (which may be eroded across the folds), style of folds and the behaviour of individual laminae within them.

Small scale faulting may also occur as a soft sediment deformation. Like the folding it will be limited in vertical extent, there will be no vein infillings of quartz, calcite or other minerals, and the fault planes will usually be 'healed up', with the matrix of the rock cemented across them so that they do not weather out as planes of weakness.

Mobilization of sediment forms a third category of pre-lithification deformation. The sediment is mobilized under a high water pressure, and is then injected into other beds. Sand is most prone to 'liquify' in this manner, mud being more cohesive. Injection may be along bedding planes, producing sills, and both upwards and downwards as *neptunean* dykes (No. 41). Exceptionally it is extruded at the sediment surface as a sand volcano. Internally all the features of igneous intrusions, apart from baking, may be produced. The dykes produced range in width from a few millimetres to several metres.

Turbidites

The sediments now interpreted as *turbidites* form an important group of siltstones, sandstones and grits, with distinctive sedimentary features. They form *graded* beds (Nos 35, 146), that is each bed becomes finer upwards from a sharp base, and ideally passes up into a muddy sediment. The base of each graded bed is often an erosive one, with a variety of scour marks and impressions caused by erosion of the underlying sea floor and by particles bouncing or dragging along. Where the sediment beneath is a fine grained mud, the marks are infilled by the coarser sediment of the graded bed, and it is these infills which are often preserved on the under surface as *bottom structures*. In a fully developed bed the lowest part is usually without obvious laminations, or simply shows parallel laminae. This may be succeeded by small scale cross bedding of the ripple drift type (No. 26). The uppermost and finest laminae are usually even bedded, and pass up into either laminated or structureless muddy sediment. Flakes of sediment (No. 43) are sometimes incorporated in the bed, and are usually lithologically indistinguishable from the rest of the sequence. *Convolute bedding* (No. 40) is also found, and is overlain by parallel laminae with a minute unconformity within the bed.

Turbidity or *density* currents can be observed today to deposit sediments of this type: they are generated when a mixture of fine mud and water flows down a submarine slope. The suspended mud increases the density of the water, enabling it to move silt, sand, shells and even pebbles, and as the mass is denser than the surrounding clear water it will move under the influence of gravity down slope. Such a slope need only be of a few degrees, and the current can reach several km/hour. It can also erode quite deeply into the sea floor, ripping up the sediment, which if sufficiently cohesive may be carried as quite large, usually plastic, rafts of material. The current, on reaching a level sea floor, will gradually lose speed, depositing first the larger and more dense particles carried, and finally the finest mud. This mechanism implies that the sediment was originally deposited in shallower water upslope (at the present day on river delta fronts, in lakes and in shallow waters on the continental shelf), and that the accumulation from time to time becomes unstable. A suitable 'trigger', such as a storm or an earthquake shock, then causes the sediment to slide downslope, and with the addition of mud collected en route, form a turbidity current. Today, the resultant turbidites are found in lakes, basins within the continental shelves, and on the ocean floors adjacent to the continents. They can be examined in sediment cores obtained by drilling into the sea floor, and have been timed where they have broken submarine cables. Small scale experimental flows have also been produced in the laboratory.

Turbidites form enormous thicknesses of sediment in the geological record, and a considerable amount of information can be obtained by examining their pebble and shell content, and determining the ancient or palaeocurrent directions from the bottom structures, ripple marks and current bedding of the sediments (Fig. 13). They are found in the sediments of many ancient fold belts: in Wales, Scotland, the Alps, Rockies and Andes, etc. In mapping these suites, it has been found that where there was an elongate basin of deposition, current directions fall into two maxima: along the axis of the basin (*axial turbidites*) and from the sides (*lateral turbidites*).

Chemical Deposits

The majority of deposits included here are formed by *precipitation* from solution, while others result from

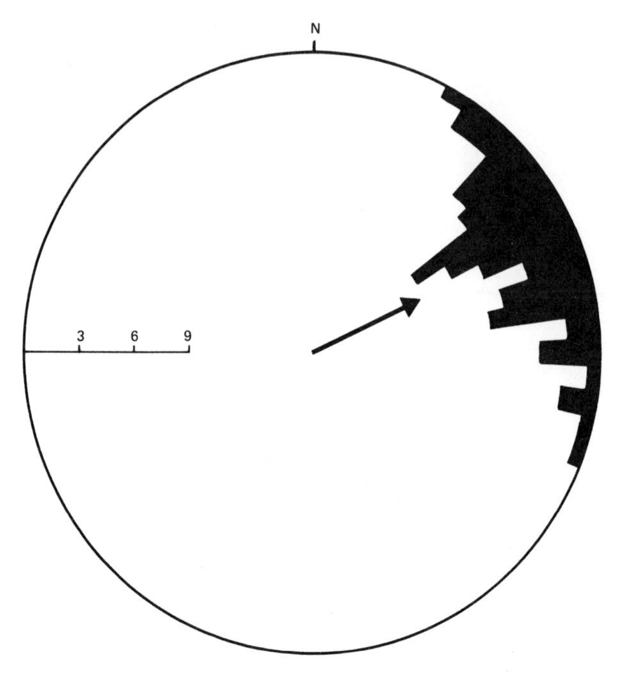

Fig. 13. *Rose diagram of current directions in a turbidite sequence. The arrow points downstream.*

replacement within the already deposited sediment (p. 60).

The most common precipitate is lime, or calcium carbonate, generally in warm shallow agitated waters (unlike most solids which dissolve in water, the solubility of lime decreases with increasing temperature). Lime is also precipitated in caves, fissures and soils in arid regions. Further details of these processes is given in a separate section below (p. 59).

Evaporites, sometimes referred to as *salines*, form an economically important group of deposits precipitated from rapidly evaporating water, either in restricted seas or enclosed inland basins. Halite (rock salt), and calcium sulphate (either without water, anhydrite, or hydrated, gypsum) are the two most widespread minerals, while others are found in small amounts. Sea water contains about 3.5% dissolved salts, of which the bulk is sodium chloride. Its evaporation will yield successively limestone and dolomite, anhydrite, rock salt and finally other potassium and magnesium salts. The exact order will depend on the composition of the water and the temperature. Though some evaporites show a sequence corresponding to that outlined above, other more complex deposits were probably laid down in fluctuating conditions, with continuous or intermittent addition of more water. The Dead Sea in the Middle East is a classic modern example.

Rock salt is a massive, coarsely crystalline rock without joints, sometimes laminated and with layers of anhydrite or gypsum. It can flow easily under pressure, giving salt domes, pipe-like intrusions rather like volcanic plugs, up to several kilometres in diameter (p. 163). These dome up the strata through which they pass, and internally show very complex folding of the salt.

Anhydrite and gypsum deposits are also finely or coarsely crystalline, massive or thinly laminated (No. 54), and sometimes with large crystals set in a fine grained groundmass. Gypsum can be found in veins in anhydrite deposits, and in many cases it is probable that gypsum deposits were originally composed of anhydrite. Swelling accompanies this change, giving local and often intense folding in some deposits. It should be noted that evaporite deposits are in some ways more akin to igneous and metamorphic rocks than to other sediments, both in the process of precipitation and in subsequent recrystallization.

Solution effects are often found with evaporite beds, since groundwater or porewater can remove them in solution, if the chemical and physical conditions are right, causing the overlying strata to collapse or distort. Highly variable folding can occur, with no tectonic preferred orientation or regularity. Additionally or alternatively, the beds may break up to form a breccia of angular blocks, such as the Broken Beds at Lulworth Cove (No. 53) or the spectacular breccias of the Durham coast (No. 55).

Organic Deposits

Organic deposits are formed of the remains of organisms, whether animal or plant, accumulating either *in situ* (as with some reef limestones) or by deposition following transport (e.g. fossil shell banks). The majority of organic deposits are in fact limestones of various types, and are dealt with in a separate section (p. 59).

Carbonaceous deposits are formed principally from terrigenous plant fragments, and range from peats through lignite or brown coal to anthracite. *In situ* deposits result from accumulation of material around the growing plants, forming a peat for as long as the vegetation cover persists. Conditions may have been relatively dry, but peat formation is favoured by swampy conditions, which prevent rapid decay of the plant (and animal) material within it. Burial of the peat beneath later sediment causes compaction, expulsion of water, and gradual removal of the nitrogen, oxygen and hydrogen to enrich the sediment in carbon. These processes are said to increase the *rank* of the coal, and the following types may be recognized, with increasing rank: peat, brown coal or lignite, bituminous coal, and anthracite.

Brown coal is brown or brownish-black, and retains the original woody texture of a peat, with easily recognized plant fragments, but higher rank coals rarely contain any easily seen plant debris. These coals are rarely homogeneous, but are finely layered, with four main components. *Vitrain* is glassy or vitreous, brittle and clean to the touch. *Fusain* is dull and powdery, and soils the fingers; it has been described as fossil charcoal. *Durain* is a dull and hard material, formed from the more resistant parts of the plants such as the spore cases. Finally *clarain* is glossy or shiny, laminated and with a silky lustre. In the higher rank coals vitrain becomes the dominant component.

In situ coals (Nos 57–60) form thin but persistent beds or seams often extending over the whole of a single coalfield with little variation in thickness. The coal is commonly underlain by a *seat earth*, a fossil clay soil penetrated by the roots of the first plants of the forest. Sometimes the underlying bed is a *ganister*, a fine quartz sandstone. The overlying sediment usually rests on the coal with an abrupt contact, and may contain traces of the trunks of the last trees to grow before the sediment, often of marine or brackish water origin, choked the forest growth (p. 48, Fig. 12).

Other coals have accumulated in water, in ponds or lakes, where the coaly material, often rich in seed cases, is mixed with silt or mud to produce a hard, dull rock called a *cannel* or *boghead* coal. It never forms extensive beds, but occurs as local lenses, sometimes within more normal coals and sometimes in lake sediments.

Land floras only became well developed in the Carboniferous, while prior to the Devonian there is very little evidence of land plants. Correspondingly there is very little evidence of coals from before the Upper Palaeozoic. There are some Pre-Cambrian coals, metamorphosed to graphite, which are thought to have been algal in origin.

Peat beds form important though thin and impersistent members of the Pleistocene and recent superficial deposits. These include forest peats, upland blanket bogs, accumulations in swamps and lakes, and soil profiles. Submerged forests are conspicuous features of parts of the British coastline; they were formed at a time of slightly lowered sea level. Fossil peats, with recognizable plant remains, including pollen, are good indicators of climatic conditions. These form much better indicators of interglacial conditions than the fluvio–glacial deposits described earlier (p. 49), and a vertical section through such a peat (Nos 154, 155) may reveal a record of changing floras recording climatic changes at the site. These peats are likely to be exposed in temporary excavations, and should be recorded and brought to the notice of a local museum, university or government geological survey.

Phosphatic sediments of organic origin are formed from vertebrate remains, and to a lesser extent from phosphatic shelled invertebrates. *Bone Beds* (No. 56) are rare features of the geological record, and suggest unusual circumstances of deposition. Mass extinction of life, by salinity changes, earthquakes or dinoflagellate outbursts (red tide) has been invoked for some bone beds. The bones, teeth and scales are either dark brown or black, shiny on their surfaces, or bleached and rough in a weathered outcrop. The more common phosphatic deposits are precipitates of nodules, either formed in agitated water rather like limestone ooliths, or in some cases within the sediment. It is possible that some phosphatic nodules may be fossil droppings (No. 9).

Siliceous organisms are all microscopic, comprising principally the diatoms (plants) and the radiolarians (animals). Their remains are found in both lakes and the deep seas, where water conditions are quiet and other sediment sparse. An even textured and very fine grained sediment results, though microscopic examination is necessary to confirm its composition. Fresh water diatoms form the lake deposits known as *diatomaceous earths*, a crumbly deposit used as an insulator. Deep sea *diatom* and *radiolarian oozes* are being deposited today, and lithified equivalents form some of the bedded cherts, though inorganically precipitated silica is a more important constituent in many cases.

Limestones and Other Carbonates

Carbonate rocks (containing more than 50% carbonate minerals) are extremely varied, both in composition and in the mechanism of deposition. The most common carbonate is lime, calcium carbonate, which exists in two crystalline forms, aragonite and the more stable calcite. Magnesium carbonate, dolomite, is also found in limestones, and if dominant over lime the rock is termed a *dolomite*.

Many calcareous rocks are clastic rocks in which the clasts are of calcareous material, such as limestone grains, pebbles or boulders (No. 10). Since limestone is comparatively soft and also soluble in acid water, such material does not travel far and indicates an immature deposit. If the clasts are composed of shell fragments (No. 46) the rock is described as a *bioclastic limestone*.

Chemical precipitation is an important process in the formation of many limestones (e.g. No. 45), both in the formation of large grains of precipitate on the sea floor, and in the crystallization of a matrix binding the rock together. Lime recrystallizes very easily, especially in the alteration of aragonite to calcite, resulting in the formation of a hard rock virtually on the sea floor, or in the precipitation of lime to form stalactites and stalagmites in caves. Consequently, it is very difficult in many cases to determine the mode of deposition of the original rock. Conversely, other limestones may escape early lithification and remain unconsolidated for long periods of time.

Oolitic limestones are formed of rounded grains of calcite, termed *ooliths*, usually set in a calcareous matrix. The ooliths themselves are formed by precipitation of carbonate in concentric layers round a nucleus, such as a sand grain or shell fragment. The process can be observed on the Bahamas Banks, where the tiny spheroids are rolled around by strong currents and wave action.

Dolomites contain magnesium carbonate, usually with lime in addition, purely dolomitic rocks being very rare. Many are secondarily enriched in dolomite, as either concretions or irregular veins along bedding planes or joints. The honey coloured dolomitized portions stand out from the more normal grey limestones in weathered outcrops. Fossils may be left undolomitized.

Chalk is an extremely pure limestone, except in the more argillaceous basal beds. It is composed of minute calcareous algae, called *coccoliths*, and commonly has concretions of chert, or flint (Nos 47, 63).

Many limestones are formed from ancient reefs. Coral reefs, such as the Great Barrier Reef of Australia, are obvious modern examples, but other organisms contribute to reefs, and may indeed be dominant. In this sense, the term reef is applied to a structure built up of organisms, not reef in the sense of a shoal or shallow water. The hard skeletons of corals, bryozoans, sponges and other organisms, and the lime trapped by algae, build up to form a resistant structure, within which sediment may be trapped, or lime gradually precipitated, to form the reef limestone. Fossil reefs can be recognized in outcrop by the meshwork of reef builders (No. 44); they also tend to resist erosion rather better than the surrounding sediments, and thus can be exhumed to form topographic features. The surrounding sediments may also be distinctive; fore-reef talus interfingering with shales on the seaward side, and back-reef lagoonal deposits, which may be sands, shales or even evaporites, on the other side (Fig. 14).

Freshwater limestones are rare, but localized deposits occur where the water is supersaturated with lime, especially in regions of calcareous rock. *Tufa* is a loosely cemented limestone associated with springs, often enclosing twigs, leaves and other objects, while *travertine* is a harder variety. Calcareous nodules are found in some sandstones of continental origin (No. 81), and may be so dense as to form limestone bands (*caliche*).

Iron carbonates, in which the mineral siderite is present, may form oolitic rocks which are important sources of iron ore. In these rocks the iron carbonate may be a metasomatic replacement of calcium carbonate, though some may have been directly precipitated as a green iron silicate, *chamosite*, which has also been replaced by siderite. In weathered outcrops the iron carbonate itself breaks down to brown limonite (No. 49). Other iron carbonates include post depositional concretions of *clay ironstone*, which may form sufficiently rich beds or layers to be commercially worked. Some of these are precipitated in non-marine conditions where the waters and sediment were stagnant (No. 59). The clayband and

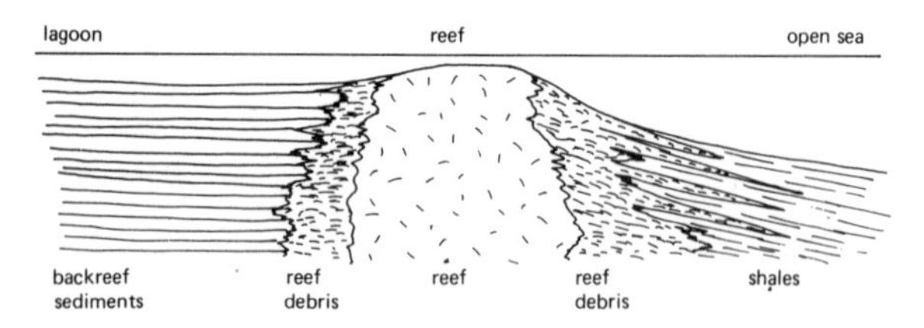

Fig. 14. *Diagrammatic cross section through a reef.*

blackband ironstones of the British Isles are good examples of this mode of origin.

Stylolites (No. 50) are interlocking surfaces found usually in limestones, but occasionally in siliceous rocks also. The term refers to the appearance of the rock in cross-section, which gives the appearance of the tracing of a stylus in an oscillogram. The surface is often marked by an accumulation of material which is relatively insoluble, such as sand or mud in a limestone. Fossils, and veins, may be cut by the stylolitic surface, indicating that the surface is one of erosion by solution of part of the strata. Material is carried away by ground water or pore water.

Chemical Structures of Secondary Origin

A number of features of sedimentary rocks, of common occurrence, and of chemical origin, are called concretions, nodules, geodes, etc. All are formed by the crystallization of solutions, within the pore water of the sediment, either replacing or being added to the rock. Generally deposition of material takes place around a nucleus, which may be a fossil, some inorganic constituent of the sediment, or simply a location already rich in the crystallizing mineral. The resulting structures tend to be spherical, ovoid, pancake-like, or irregular growths with curved surfaces and very varied shapes. Burrows in the sediment may be infilled, giving oddly shaped concretions, like some flints in the Chalk of England.

Strictly, nodules have no internal structure, and may have been formed by complete replacement of the host rock. The most common types are the nodules of *flint* or *chert* (the terms are largely interchangeable) found in many limestones (Nos 63, 64). They are formed of extremely fine grained silica, in which small fossils may be found still composed of lime. *Concretions* are formed by the precipitation in the pore spaces of mineral matter around a nucleus, the original sedimentary layering passing through the concretion without disturbance (No. 61). Geodes are hollow growths, usually subspherical, lined by crystals projecting inwards.

Cone-in-cone structure (No. 62) is another feature of apparent chemical origin, often found in these accretionary bodies, but also within layers of sediment. In both cases the layers of sediment and precipitate are disposed in conical formation, with circular wrinkles on the surfaces. In beds the cones lie apex-downwards, while in concretions the apices point inwards.

The chemistry of all these growths is very poorly understood, as it is almost impossible to observe their growth. Cone-in-cone structure is thought to be connected with pressure, perhaps the pressure of a concretion swelling against the sediment as it grows. Conversely cracks, infilled with later crystals, are found in some concretions (septarian nodules), suggesting shrinkage during part of their development (No. 65).

Fossils in Field Work

Although fossils are studied by palaeontologists as organisms of interest in their own right (palaeozoology and palaeobotany), in field work we are mainly concerned with the applied aspects of fossils: for determining the age of the strata, as indicators of the environment of deposition, and as sedimentary particles. Virtually all fossils are of some use for geological dating, though those which were evolving rapidly, and therefore had a short time range, are much more useful. The occurrence and abundance of the fossils should be carefully noted: where vertical sections are recorded these details can be added. Similarly, any fossils collected should be carefully labelled to correspond with detailed map and notebook references. It should be possible for a subsequent collector, using this information, to identify a particular fossiliferous horizon to within a centimetre or less even in a large exposure, if this is necessary.

Derived fossils (Nos 8, 9) may be difficult to detect. They may have been partially worn during transport from their original rock, or may contrast with those which really belong to the strata of the outcrop. The greater the age gap between the two suites of fossils, the easier it will be to detect the presence of the derived fossils. They may also have been phosphatized.

The nature of the fossils, and their distribution within the rock, can yield a great deal of information about the environment in which the rocks were deposited (No. 44), while as an area is mapped the environments of one or more geological age can be plotted to give a map of the palaeogeography or successive palaeogeographies of the region. Firstly, obviously derived fossils must be discounted (except that they may provide information about a source rock for the sediment). Secondly, a clear distinction must be made between fossils which are *in situ*, in growth position, and those which have accumulated after death. In the first category fall corals on a reef structure, and other animals cemented to a substratum (No. 48), or entombed in a burrow, and plants such as root structures and stromatolites (calcareous mounds precipitated under the influence of benthonic algae). Their attitude may help to determine the direction of the palaeocurrents, their relationships to each other something about symbiosis or competition between species or individuals. More commonly the fossils have accumulated after death, and are to some extent 'derived', but derived from local sources, and geologically of the same age as the enclosing rock. This is almost inevitably the case where the animals were active, such as vertebrates, or swimming invertebrates like ammonites. Accordingly, the remains have been transported and to some extent sorted by the sedimentary processes of transportation and deposition.

Fossils form very sensitive current indicators, as their distinctive shapes respond in characteristic ways to movement by water. Crinoid stems and other cylindrical fossils will roll downcurrent and may come to rest either when they swing round to point up and down current, or roll against a stationary object. Graptolites are often similarly aligned. Other fossils, such as brachiopods or bivalves, may not show such a spectacular alignment (No. 46), but measurement of the orientation of a large number may yield a significant pattern. Other measurements are possible; convex shells or valves will tend to accumulate with their convex side uppermost, while the ratio between the two valves of a bivalve or brachiopod may depart from 1:1 if the assemblage has been transported. In rocks which are structurally complex, the original 'way-up' can also be determined by observation of these features.

Trace fossils form a separate category of fossils, whose study has become a specialized branch of both palaeontology and sedimentology (palaeoichnology). They are defined by palaeontologists as the traces left by the life activities of animals. Included are tracks or trails, such as footprints made on the surface of the sediment (No. 25), and a variety of burrows (Nos 20, 66–68), made within sediment by animals either as dwellings or in search of food.

Surface trails can be preserved where further sediment is laid down over the trails, without any scouring of the surface. Similarly dwelling burrows can be filled with sediment after the death of the occupant. Many burrowers move extensively through the sediment (No. 69), actually eating it to extract any contained food, and backfilling the burrow behind them, or venting the waste on the surface. A wide variety of often elaborate burrow systems has been recognized. Many of these are localized at bedding planes between two types of sediments, often where coarse sediment overlies an organically rich mud (No. 71). Other burrow systems are not limited to one bedding plane, but form complex three-

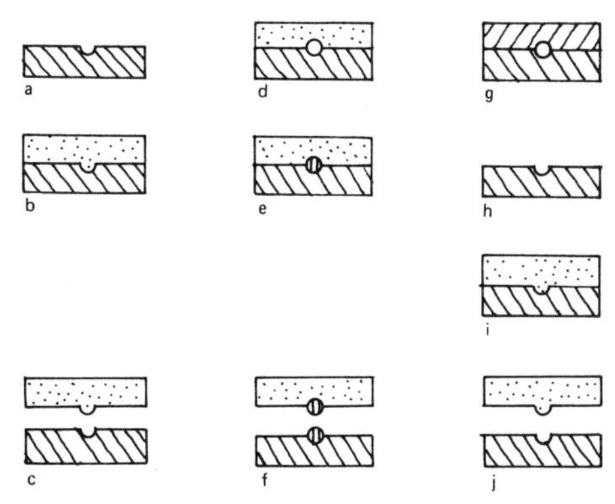

Fig. 15. *The preservation of trails and burrows.* a *Trail on sea floor.* b *Trail infilled with sediment.* c *Trail preserved on under surface as ridge, and on top surface as depression.* d *Burrow along bedding plane between two sediments.* e *Burrow infilled with sediment.* f *Burrow infilling adhering to either sediment.* g *Burrow along bedding plane between two sediments.* h *Sediment above burrow and any burrow infilling removed by current scour down to bedding plane.* i *Half-removed burrow infilled by more sediment.* j *Preservation of burrow similar to that of trail in* c.

dimensional networks. Little is is known about the animals responsible: skeletal remains are not found with most types of burrows, hence they were probably soft bodied worm-like creatures. Such burrows are difficult to study on modern sea floors. Virtually the only method is to pour a quick-setting plastic into the burrow system, and pull it out after hardening, perhaps with the luckless burrower also caught.

Separation of different trace fossil types is often difficult, especially where they occur on interfaces between different sediment types, as at the base of a turbidite. Figure 15 illustrates some of the difficulties which may arise.

Besides telling us how certain animals lived, trace fossils can indicate different types of environments, and have been used to differentiate between shallow and deep water sediments. They can also give the order of deposition in overturned strata (p. 42). Stratigraphically they have been little used, since very similar burrows and trails have been found in rocks of widely different ages. It appears that particular types of trace fossil reflect particular life activities, and hence change little with evolutionary changes. Unlike normal or body fossils, they cannot become derived fossils. At some horizons, particularly in the younger Pre-Cambrian, trace fossils are the only evidence of life to be found.

Trace fossils and body fossils are not often found together. Because of this separation it is seldom that a particular trace fossil can be assigned to a producer. In some cases the trace fossils may be due to soft bodied animals, whose remains are not easily preserved. This is particularly true of burrowing animals, such as lugworms, for whom the burrow, rather than a carapace, is a protection. In other environments the hard parts may have been destroyed before burial, perhaps by solution in the sea water.

Breaks in Deposition and Unconformities

Breaks in deposition of sediment, during which erosion often takes place, can occur on all scales, from a break between tides in shallow water deposits, to a major unconformity between two series of rocks, where the gap between them represents millions of years and a multitude of geological events (Fig. 16).

Small scale breaks in deposition commonly occur where bedding planes separate units of sediment. Even successive bedding planes mark at least a pause in sedimentation. Where erosion also occurs, the breaks are clearer, particularly if foreset beds are truncated. Examples can be seen in Nos 19 and 21, of aeolian and subaqueous cross bedding, where each set of beds is succeeded by an erosional break. The erosive features seen at the base of some turbidites (No. 36) are evidence of another type of break in deposition.

At the other extreme the spectacular unconformity, where there is a conspicuous angular relationship between the two rock groups involved (an *angular unconformity*), is easy to recognize in the field (Figs 16a, 22; No. 18). It may be an irregular surface (Fig. 16f), giving some clue to the topography of the land surface buried by the younger sediments, or may indeed be a *plane* of unconform-

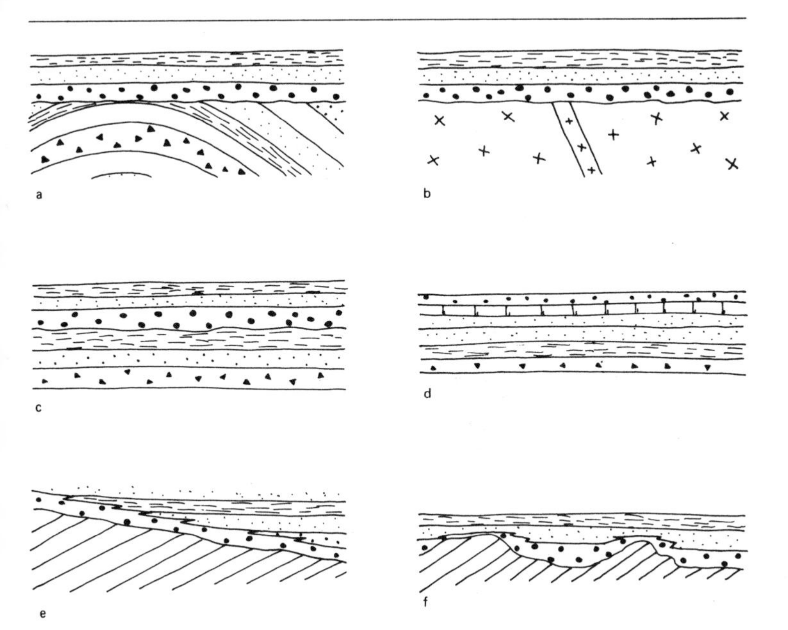

Fig. 16. *Types of unconformity.* a *Angular unconformity.* b *Nonconformity on igneous rocks.* c *Disconformity with obvious erosion surface and basal conglomerate.* d *Disconformity with little indication of break in sedimentation.* e *Diachronous transgression.* f *Unconformity on surface with considerable relief.*

ity, essentially flat within the limits of the exposure (No. 18), or even when mapped. Such surfaces can be studied in the process of formation, on present day lake and sea shores, in river valleys, and on land surfaces where the soils and other superficial deposits could become the basal sediments of a new sedimentary suite. A basal conglomerate may be found resting on the surface of unconformity, formed from the pebble or boulder beach deposits of the advancing sea, though it is much less often developed than would appear from many geological textbooks. The basal beds may be *diachronous* (Fig. 16e), not everywhere of the same age, but becoming younger as a surface of the older rocks is gradually submerged by the advancing transgression. If the underlying rocks are not sedimentary, the term *nonconformity* is sometimes applied (Fig. 16b).

Occasionally there is no angular discrepancy between the two series of rocks, and the younger series rests with apparent conformity or concordance on the older. This situation is called a *disconformity* (Fig. 16c), and can be quite difficult to detect. There may be small scale erosion of the older rocks (e.g. in the sequence of No. 24), and pebbles derived from the older series may be emplaced in the younger. Phosphatic nodules are another characteristic feature of these breaks (e.g. No. 9). The fossil contents of the two series can sometimes be used to separate them by demonstrating a gap in the fossil record. A hazard which occurs here is the erosion of fossils from the older series and their deposition in the younger. These *derived fossils* (p. 62) can of course be found away from unconformities as well. Finally, mapping of the boundary between the series can reveal an angular relationship on the map where none is evident in the field in exposures. A difference between the two series of 1° will be very difficult to detect in outcrop, yet will cut out 60m of beds in 1km, in a direction at right angles to the line of intersection between the two planes. If the outcrop of the unconformity is parallel to the line of intersection, there will of course be almost no angular difference between the two series, even in mapping. It should also be noted that a difference between the series of 1–3° will not be detected using a compass/clinometer as it will be masked by inaccuracies in the instrument and the irregular surfaces of the bedding planes measured.

4 GEOLOGICAL STRUCTURES

Folds

Layers of sediment initially show a horizontal stratification, unless an original dip, as in dune bedding (No. 19), is present. This means that, provided the originally horizontal bedding is recognizable, we can measure the amount of tilting, folding or distortion that the rock has undergone. To be present in outcrop, on land (that is not below sea level), marine rocks must at least have been raised to their present position. Rarely this is accomplished without any tilting of the layering, purely by uplift, or to a small degree by lowering of sea level (No. 10). More commonly, however, such uplift is accompanied by, and is probably subordinate to, at least gentle warping or folding of the strata.

Folding (Figs 17, 18) involves a shortening in one direction, perpendicular to the fold axes. In general this is thought to be caused by a compression in this direction, with a relief of pressure upwards (against gravity) to produce the anticlines or upfolds, and usually no significant change in dimensions along the fold axes, but rather a rotation of the fold limbs about this direction. Gentle folding is usually large scale, with fold hinges perhaps miles apart, and very low dips on the limbs. In southern England the Wealden anticline and the London basin are examples of this type of fold. Although many folds may be caused by lateral pressure, parallel to the earth's crust, these gentle large folds could also be the result of purely gravity forces – sags in the crust of the earth beneath.

Fold geometry is illustrated in Fig. 17. The *axis* (or *axial line*) is an imaginary line joining the points of maximum curvature of any one bedding plane passing over the fold; an imaginary plane or curved surface containing the axes in different beds is termed the *axial plane* or *axial surface*. In many folds the axial plane is vertical and the axis horizontal, and in this situation the dip is the

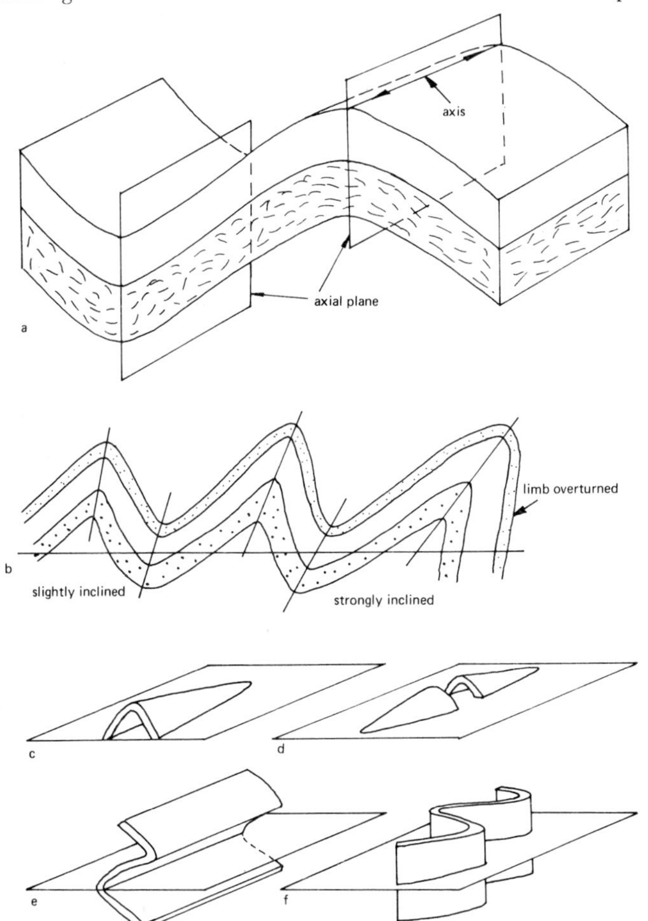

Fig. 17. *Fold types.* a *Upright.* b *Inclined.* c *Plunging.* d *Periclinal.* e *Recumbent.* f *Neutral.*

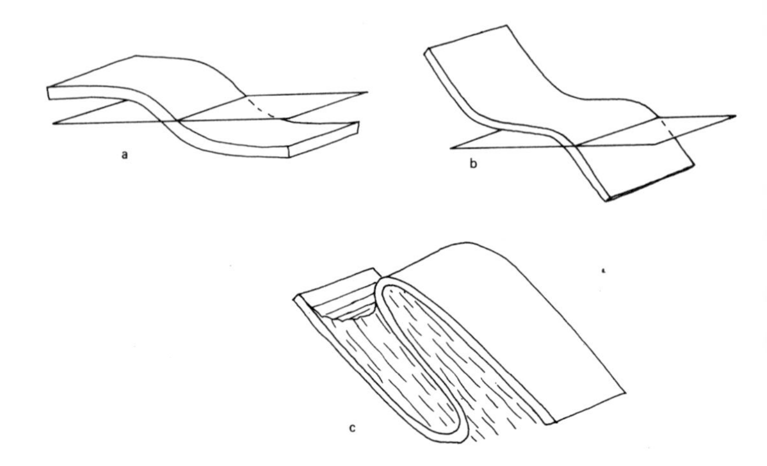

Fig. 18. *Fold types.* a *Monocline.* b *Structural terrace.* c *Isocline.*

same on the two sides or limbs of the folds, and so is the direction of strike. This will hold for both an anticline or upfold, and a syncline or downfold. In many cases the axial plane also bisects the angle between the limbs of the fold. The processes by which the rocks are deformed during the production of folds vary with the physical state of the rocks, and the intensity of the force applied; in addition the physical state of the rock may change during the formation of the fold (e.g. the minerals may recrystallize or pore water may be driven out). As a result many different kinds of folds have been recognized, and a specialized terminology developed to describe them.

Folds need not always be symmetrical structures as outlined above. If the folds of Fig. 17a are tilted sideways, so that the axial plane is not vertical, but the axis is still horizontal, they are said to be *inclined* (Fig. 17b). If they are tilted so that the axial plane is horizontal, they become *recumbent*. Alternatively, they may be tilted so that the axial plane remains vertical, but the axis is no longer horizontal, and are then described as *plunging* (Fig. 17c). The angle of plunge may be vertical, when the folds become *neutral*, or *sideways-closing* (Fig. 17f). Both processes may operate together, to form folds which are both inclined and plunging. *Monoclines* (Fig. 18a) are 'one-sided' folds, zones of dipping rock in an otherwise horizontal series of beds. Conversely, a *structural terrace* is a zone of horizontal beds in dipping strata (Fig. 18b).

More severe folding results in 'tighter' folds, with steeper dips on the limbs, and in many cases the individual folds can be seen in outcrops. Additionally, both large and small folds occur together. The minor folds are often small scale replicas of the larger, so much so that the field geologist may use them as a key to deciphering the major folds (p. 40). Commonly these smaller folds occur in pairs, an anticline and a syncline close together. The synclinal hinge lies nearer the axis of the major anticline, the anticlinal axis nearer the axis of the syncline. The axes of these folds are generally parallel to the axis of the major folds, as are the axial planes.

A single fold structure – anticline or syncline – cannot have an infinite length along its axis, but must die out in both directions. As a result, the folds do not appear like a corrugated iron sheet, but a complicated jumble of structures like double ended boats, upside down for the anticlines and right way up for the synclines. The folds are all interlocking in a complex way, but all will normally have parallel axial planes, whose strike gives the trend of the fold belt. Individual anticlines will have horizontal axes in the middle of the structure, but away from this the axis will plunge in opposite directions. The converse is true for synclines. Such folding is called *periclinal.* If a region shows a constant plunge of the fold axes in one direction, this may be the result of a wholesale tilting of the area, after the folds have been formed, by subsequent earth movements.

Slaty, or axial plane cleavage, is often associated with tight folding: its presence is a clue to the intensity of compression suffered by the strata. It is formed by a rotation of the platy minerals, usually clay minerals or micas, into parallelism with one another, perpendicular to the direction of maximum pressure or stress. As this pressure is usually that causing the folding at the same time, these planes tend to be parallel to the axial planes of the folds forming, hence the term axial plane cleavage. In some cases, the cleavage may 'fan' about the hinge of the fold, this being well illustrated in No. 91 and Fig. 37. *Isoclinal folding* (No. 83), in which the limbs of the fold are parallel to each other, the axial plane, and the cleavage, is commonly found in tightly folded terrain.

The individual mineral grains of a rock showing slaty cleavage, a slate, are small and closely packed. This allows the slate to be split along planes which are very closely spaced, and this is aided by the good cleavage *within* individual crystals of the clay minerals. Slaty cleavage is often regarded as an indication of low grade metamorphism (see p. 146), and slightly increased pressure and temperature will lead into the regime of metamorphic folds proper. Coarser sediments, with equidimensional grains, show a much less well developed cleavage than the associated fine grained sediments (No. 74). Spaced fracture planes may be formed (No. 81), the sediment between remaining relatively undeformed (*fracture cleavage*). Small displacements may be found across individual fractures, suggesting that each acted as a minute fault plane.

As already mentioned, folding of beds may be due to other causes than post depositional tectonic shortening, for example, convolution in glacial or periglacial deposits (p. 51), slumping (p. 53), collapse due to the solution of evaporites (p. 57), etc. Such folding is usually restricted to definite layers of limited thickness, the over and underlying beds being unaffected (Nos 37, 40), whilst the fact that the beds have been deposited in an environment in which contemporaneous or penecontemporaneous disturbances might occur should be apparent from the study of their lithology.

Faults

Faults are geological structures which are produced by fracture or breakage of the rock, and consequent slip of the rock masses on either side of the break (the *fault plane*). Often brecciation of the rock occurs producing angular blocks cemented with minerals crystallized from solution in pore water (a *fault breccia*). Quartz and calcite are most commonly found: they reflect the dominance of these minerals in the rocks which are faulted. Calcite is generally found in calcareous rocks, or those which have a calcareous matrix, quartz in both quartzose and argillaceous rocks. Other minerals, including ore minerals (particularly copper, lead and zinc sulphides) may be present, and many metalliferous mines have been sited on faults (e.g. No. 156).

The fault surface may be striated (No. 84), the striations reflecting at least some of the movement on the fault. They may be simply grooves or gouges, formed by the rubbing of one rock surface on the other, but more commonly they are elongated mineral fibres, which are formed by the *growth* of the minerals, and not the destruction of material. In this respect they indicate that the two faces of the rock masses have actually moved apart to allow the minerals to be precipitated between them. This may imply a very high pore water pressure during the faulting. The term *slickensiding* has often been used for both phenomena, but should be restricted to imply a polished and gouged surface, while *growth fibres* should be applied to the constructive feature. Crushing of the rock may produce a *gouge*, a zone of finely ground and smashed rock fragments, which has not been recemented.

A majority of faults dip at a high angle, and thus form tolerably straight outcrops, which are only slightly affected by topographic changes (p. 39). Where they strike parallel to the strike of the beds (as in Fig. 19a–b) they are referred to as *strike faults*. Faults which strike approximately perpendicular to the strike of the beds, as do those in the sample field area (No. 156), are *dip faults*. Note that these terms should not be confused with *strike-slip* and *dip-slip* faults (see below).

Fault planes can have any orientation, but most faults examined fall into one of three categories (Fig. 19). *Normal faults*, so-called because of their commonness, dip at a high angle, and one block of rock drops down in relation to the other, due to relative tension at right angles to the outcrop of the fault. Gravity forms the greatest pressure. A downfaulted block between parallel but opposing normal faults forms a *rift valley*, or *graben*, while the converse, an upfaulted block, is termed a *horst*.

Both the other types of fault are caused by horizontally directed compressive stress. If the relief of pressure can be upwards (against gravity) then low-dipping *thrust faults* are formed, with striations inclined down the dip of the fault plane.

Reverse faults, dipping at a higher angle, may also be produced in this situation. Both normal and reverse faults are *dip-slip faults*, since the direction of movement is parallel to the dip of the fault plane.

If the relief of pressure upwards is not possible, due usually to a thick overburden, then horizontal movement may occur along vertical *wrench* (*tear* or *transcurrent*) faults, and relief of pressure will be sideways.

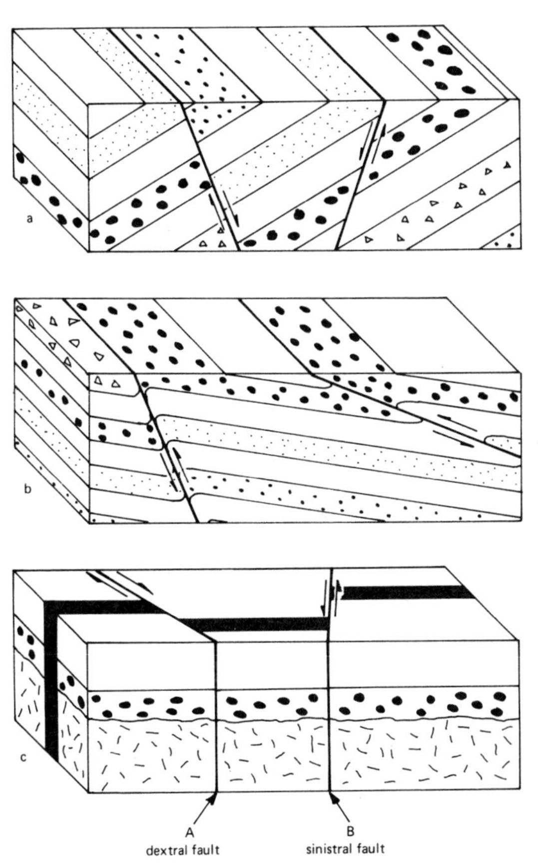

Fig. 19. *Block diagrams to illustrate the three main types of faults.* a *Normal faults.* b *Low-dipping thrust and high-dipping reverse fault.* c *Tear faults showing displacement of a vertical dyke but no displacement of a horizontal unconformity.*

The fault planes will then be vertical, and bear horizontal striations. For this reason they are sometimes called *strike-slip faults*. The direction of throw of a tear fault is ascertained by standing on one side of the fault, and observing the relative direction of movement of the other side. Thus in Fig. 19c the direction of movement of fault A is to the right, and it is described as *right-handed* or *dextral*, while fault B is *left-handed* or *sinistral*.

Faults which don't fall into these categories are few, and are called *oblique*, or *oblique-slip*, faults. They result either from special stresses, not aligned either horizontally or vertically, or when pre-existing lines of weakness, joints or faults, accommodate the slip. *Bedding plane slip*, that is fault movement parallel to the bedding planes, falls into this latter category. It often occurs during folding, as successive beds slip over one another to accommodate the distortion.

The stresses that cause faulting can also produce *tension veins* or *gashes* (No. 90). They have a lens-shaped cross-section, often twisted into a sigmoidal shape, and are infilled with quartz, calcite, etc., as with many fault breccias. The veins have a characteristic geometry in relation to the faults (Fig. 36), and can be used in analysis of the stresses.

Faults are also found in unconsolidated material, such as lake clays and glacial deposits (No. 17). Similarly, some faults in consolidated rocks may have been propagated when the sediment was still soft (p. 54). In these conditions faulting will occur when the rate of deformation is sufficiently great, and paradoxically where the sediment had not sufficient strength to buckle, though the situation is a complex one. In glacial sediments it is possible that faulting could have taken place while the rock was frozen.

Although faults are fractures, while folds show bending and sometimes stretching and distortion of the rock, the two types of structure grade into one another (No. 90). A fault may develop along the crest of a fold, the rock snapping as the bend tightens. Inclined and overturned folds may pass into thrusts (Nos 92, 93). A fault at depth in hard crystalline rocks can pass up into a flexure in younger and more pliable rocks above, this being described as a *basement and cover* relationship.

Jointing

The term *joint* is frequently used in geological literature, often with a preface, such as *tension joint* or *shear joint*, to describe a variety of surfaces of differing appearance and mode of formation. The term is used here without a preface to describe surfaces of fracture in the rock, along which there has been no appreciable movement, either shear movement (as in a fault), or movement apart of the walls (as in a vein or fissure). Commonly, such joints have no mineral infilling, apart from films of iron oxide or other minerals precipitated during weathering, and the face of the joint is either smooth or bears fine plumose or feather markings (No. 105).

In well-bedded rocks, joints usually occur in two sets, mutually perpendicular to one another and to the bedding planes (No. 103). Sometimes, in folded rocks, one set may be perpendicular to the fold axis, while the other set varies in attitude across the folds, but is everywhere perpendicular to the bedding planes and parallel to the fold axis (Fig. 11). Across the axis of the fold, where the radius of curvature of the beds is small, these joints may open as tension joints.

In many massive rocks, such as granites, three sets of mutually perpendicular joints can be present. One set may be parallel to the margins of the intrusion, and related to the frozen planes of flowage, or changing composition and texture or the marginal region. Other joints tend to develop parallel to and perpendicular to the ground surface, and these may be a consequence of the gradual stripping of over-burden to the present ground level. Those joints parallel to the ground surface are termed *sheeting joints*, and with the other sets of joints control the weathering and denudation of the land surface, producing features like the castellated granite tors and the cliff scenery of south-west England (No. 121). The jointing found in some lava flows, sills and dykes (No. 128), is related to the cooling of the hot, but solid rock. The hexagonal *columnar joints* of some lava flows are of this type (No. 118), and are analogous to the mud cracks formed when a layer of muddy sediment dries out and cracks.

Joints can also develop during faulting, presumably as a consequence of the same forces that cause the faulting. This can be observed both in outcrop, where joints may be closely spaced and aligned in a particular direction close to an exposed fault (No. 90), and in mapping the same relationships may be verified on a regional scale.

Veining

A *vein* may be defined as a crack, usually roughly planar, in the rock completely or partially infilled by one or more minerals. The term is sometimes used to describe small scale injections of igneous rock (i.e. small dykes or sills), but is more commonly restricted to cases where the infilling material was precipitated from solution (hydrothermal) or from gases rich in chemicals (pneumatolytic), not solidified from a magma.

Veins are of widespread occurrence, as can be seen in some of the illustrations. When they contain ore minerals they are often referred to as *mineralized veins* or *lodes*, though strictly speaking any natural infilling is a mineral. Examination of many veins indicates that the infilling mineral usually reflects the composition of the enclosing rock, principally calcite (in limestones and basic igneous rocks) or quartz (in sandstones and other siliceous sediments, and in acid igneous rocks). Thus, in many cases, the infilling is very locally derived, the pore water being rich in the dominant mineral, which is precipitated wherever space is available. This is found in fault zones, tension cracks (p. 72), cavities formed by solution, shell interiors unfilled by sediment, and vesicles in igneous rocks.

Crystallization of minerals usually proceeds from the walls of the vein towards the centre, often with zones marked by different impurities, or by the precipitation of different minerals (No. 99). A cavity or *vug* may be left, lined with well formed crystals (the prized minerals of the collector may well come from such a site).

Hot gases and liquids associated with large scale intrusions are responsible for many of the more spectacular veins and lodes, often with the emplacement of important ore minerals, and in this case the vein mineralogy may differ markedly from that of the enclosing rock. The increased temperature also causes soaking or penetration of the vein walls, with emplacement of minerals in zones around the actual veins (No. 101).

5 IGNEOUS ROCKS

The igneous rocks are those transported as molten liquids and 'deposited' or emplaced when this solidifies. *Ignis*, the Latin word for fire, suggests that they are burning, but the vapour or steam given off by a volcano is not the product of fire, but more akin to the steaming of heated water. In fact steam is an important constituent of these vapours. The igneous rocks include the *extrusive* rocks, which have reached the earth's surface before solidifying, and erupted from a volcano or fissure, and the *intrusive*, which have solidified within the earth's crust. Solid debris may also be ejected by a volcano, and this material is technically a sedimentary deposit, termed a *pyroclastic* rock.

Just as the sedimentary rocks are found in distinctive associations, so the igneous rocks, both intrusive and extrusive, tend to occur in characteristic suites, defined by their chemistry and mode of extrusion or emplacement. Similarly, just as the law of superposition governs the relative chronology of the sedimentary rocks, so a relative chronology can be built up for the igneous rocks, based on cross-cutting relationships (e.g. No. 129), chilled margins, and inclusions of xenoliths of one rock type in another.

Extrusive Rocks

The most spectacular manifestation of modern vulcanism is the great cone-shaped volcano, such as Fujiyama or Etna. Lava may pour out of the central crater, or subsidiary cones on the flanks, and the cone itself is formed of a mixture of solidified lava, and volcanic agglomerate: solid material, both of lava and of blocks of rock plucked off the wall of the feeder pipe, and blasted out by gas pressure. Beyond the cone, lava may spread out over more level ground, or into the sea, and ashes fall, principally downwind, to form tuffs, either wind or waterlain.

Basic and intermediate lava is relatively fluid, and will flow easily over the land surface to form plateau basalts or other lavas over wide areas of country. Often it is extruded not from a circular volcanic vent or volcano, but from a series of locations along a fissure, without any major cone being built up. In contrast acid volcanoes rarely extrude liquid lava. Instead eruption is explosive, a mixture of hot rock fragments and gases issues as a glowing cloud, or *nué ardente*, which can reach a ground speed of 100 km/hour. The material forms a coarse tuff or fine agglomerate when deposited, an aggregation of variable-sized particles that is described as an *ash-flow tuff* or an *ignimbrite*. If the deposit is thick enough and the particles hot enough, they may weld together as the cloud comes to rest and settles, in part of the tuff, to form a hard lava-like rock, a *welded tuff*. Many deposits of this kind were originally described as rhyolitic lavas, as in the flattened and welded portions the appearance is very similar to that of an acid lava. It should be noted that flattened particles (No. 107) do not in themselves indicate welding, but only flattening, and true welding is only verifiable in a thin section. True acid lavas are very fine grained and usually finely flow-banded, or even dark and glassy (*pitchstone*) if they have cooled too quickly for crystals to form.

An extinct volcano soon loses its characteristic shape and the whole cone may be eroded away and not buried to become solid rock. Hence it is rare to find a complete volcanic cone in the geological record, instead only parts are usually preserved and eventually exposed. It is more common to find the feeder pipe now standing up as a circular or oval hill, termed a *volcanic neck* or *plug* (Nos 104, 110). The presence of coarse volcanic material, agglomerate, is a good guide to the nearby presence of a volcano, for such material is too coarse to have travelled far.

Lava flows have a normal crystalline igneous texture, generally fine grained although large crystals or phenocrysts may be present, and have probably grown before extrusion. It is not always easy to distinguish between an ancient lava flow and a sill or dyke (where the interbedded strata are dipping steeply). The base of the flow may have a rubbly texture, with charring of any vegetation (No. 116). The centre of the flow will have cooled more slowly, producing an even-textured rock with a larger grain size, and with well developed cooling joints. Above is a second zone of rubbly lava, with irregular joints, while at the top there may be a weathered zone. In contrast the intrusions may have similar bottom and top contacts, with chilling of the igneous rock and baking of the country rock above (Nos 125, 126) as well as below. Unfortunately the margins of both intrusions and extrusions are often badly weathered and covered with soil and scree (No. 114).

Submarine extrusion of lava, particularly of basic material, often results in the magma separating into large globules, which are flattened against one another on the sea floor as *pillows* (Nos 119, 120). The skin of the pillow may have a slaggy 'piecrust' texture, with the centre of harder, more slowly and evenly cooled lava. The material between the pillows is either caught up from the sea floor during the eruption, or deposited in voids left between the pillows. Brecciated pillows form a distinctive volcanic breccia termed a *hyaloclastite*.

Most submarine flows of basalt are enriched in sodium, to give a petrologically distinct rock termed a *spilite*, rich in sodic feldspar. When associated with cherts, black shales, and a variety of basic intrusions, the entire association is termed an *ophiolite suite*, and is thought to have been part of a former ocean floor, and underlying oceanic crust (No. 119). Conversely pillow lavas can form in extremely shallow waters, in lakes and shelf seas (No. 120), but then lack these distinctive allies.

Pyroclastic Rocks

Pyroclastic rocks are found in three situations, within volcanic pipes or fissures, forming part of the cone, and as deposits spreading out beyond the site of the eruption. They are composed of fragments of the country rock and of solidified magma, either carried out of the vent as solid particles or flung into the air as liquid drops and solidifying in flight (*volcanic bombs*).

Agglomerate is the volcanic equivalent of conglomerate, an aggregate of blocks set in a finer matrix. Commonly the blocks are extremely angular, and very variable in size, grading down to fine material so that there is no sharp division between framework and matrix. Within a pipe or fissure the material is not usually graded, and is not laminated. It may be composed entirely of igneous material, but can include sedimentary blocks, often thermally metamorphosed, plucked off the sides of the vent or broken up by explosive activity. Exceptionally, the material may be entirely sedimentary in origin.

The material forming the volcanic cone is usually less chaotic: it may be graded and crudely bedded (No. 111), since most of it will have been ejected into the air. It will vary in grain size from coarse agglomerate to finer *ash* depending on its position on the cone and on the intensity of the eruption. Any wind blowing may influence its distribution. These air-fall ashes may also contain volcanic bombs, which tend to have a spindle shape due to their cooling in flight.

Volcanic ashes distributed beyond the cone are much better sorted, and finer grained. Fine material can be carried for many kilometres, indeed some dust may reach the upper atmosphere to be distributed globally. Water lain ashes will show some of the characters of normal clastic sediments. Bedding can be well defined (No. 109), and current bedding and other sedimentary features may be present. Indeed only the volcanic composition of the rock may give a clue as to its origin, since these ashes may be interbedded with normal sediments. Occasional large blocks may disturb the layering, as they fell through the water, and fossils may be found. These ashes are often referred to as *volcani-clastic* sediments. *Pumice* blocks, fragments of very vesicular lava often lighter than water, may be found with smaller particles of denser lava or sedimentary rock.

Since the volcanic cone itself is often removed by erosion the agglomerate and ashes preserved and indurated are usually either from within the vent or pipe (No. 110) or from waterlain sequences which were not subjected to subaerial erosion (No. 109). The indurated ashes are termed *tuff*.

Intrusive Rocks

The intrusive rocks cannot be observed in the process of emplacement, and we must infer these processes from the rocks now in outcrop. The alterations made in the surrounding, or country rocks, also yield valuable information. Three main types of intrusion occur (Fig. 20):

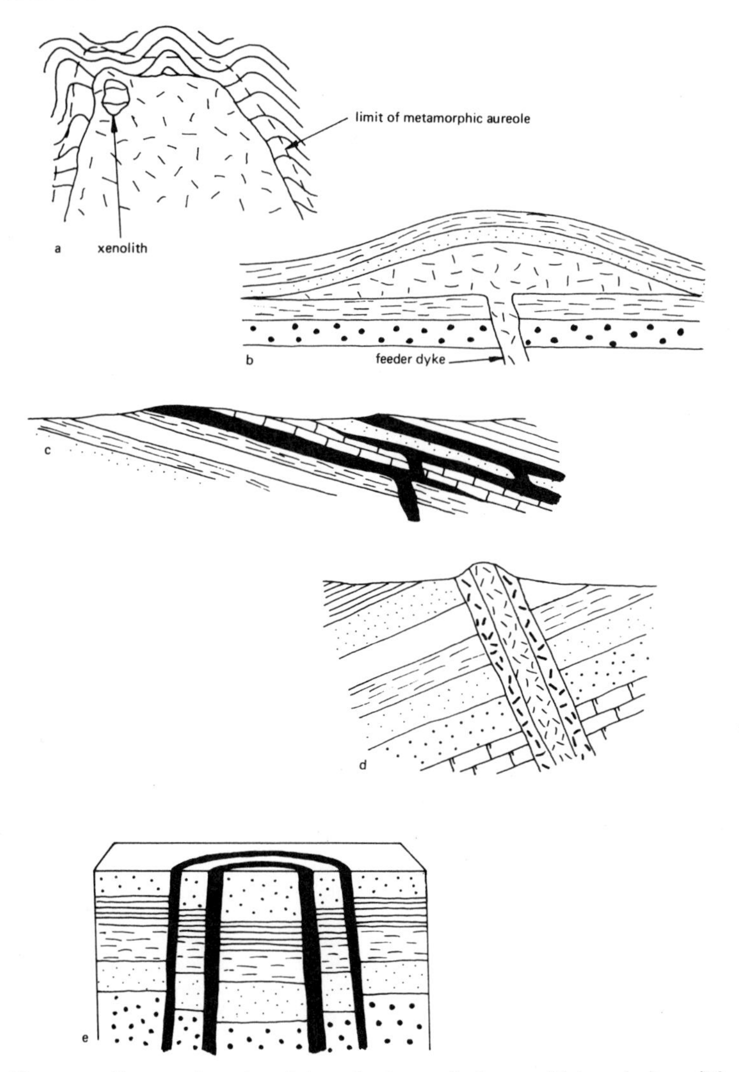

Fig. 20. *Cross sections through intrusive igneous bodies.* a *Pluton.* b *Laccolith.* c *Inclined and transgressive sills.* d *Multiple dyke.* e *Ring dykes.*

1. Large bodies (*plutons*) which have been emplaced either by shouldering aside or replacing the country rock. Huge intrusions up to tens of kilometres in length or width, are referred to as *batholiths*, while smaller intrusions are called *stocks*, or *bosses* when they have a circular outcrop. Cutting across the strata or banding of the country rock, they are described as *discordant* intrusions. Other large intrusions which are emplaced between near horizontal layers of country rock are described as *laccoliths*, pushing up the layers above like a huge blister.

2. Small concordant intrusions in horizontal to moderately dipping rocks are *sills*.

3. Near vertical intrusions infilling fissures, the intrusion having a wall-like form, are *dykes*. They indicate tension in the crust, and often occur in swarms. In fact there are all variations between vertical and horizontal intrusions, and dykes commonly act as feeders to sills at a higher level, or even to lava in a fissure eruption, the dyke underlying the fissure. Any pre-existing breaks or discontinuities in the country rocks can also act as channelways for injection, and the location of intrusions.

Ring dykes and *cone sheets* are two types of dyke associated together or separately with larger intrusions, probably bosses, at depth. Ring dykes (Fig. 20) form in ring fractures which are vertical or slope steeply outwards and downwards from the centre of the ring. Space for the magma is created by the rock within the rings subsiding. Conversely in cone sheets (Fig. 51) the hydrostatic pressure causes the overlying rocks to fracture in a series of concentric cones, up which magma is then forced. Using the dip of the sheets, as well as their position, the depth to the intrusion can then be calculated.

Note that a magma usually makes room for small to intermediate scale intrusions by physically pushing aside the country rocks, under the hydrostatic pressure of the magma. If the crust is under horizontal tension, vertical dykes will result, while lifting of the overburden will allow horizontal sills to form. Where near vertical strata have dykes intruded parallel to the bedding it is a moot point whether they should be termed sills or dykes.

In studying intrusive rocks in the field, we can divide our observations into the determination of the igneous rock type, and observation of the manner of intrusion and its effect on the country rock. Unlike extrusive rocks, many intrusions have cooled slowly enough to allow large crystals to form, so that each crystal can be identified approximately by the naked eye or with a hand lens, and relations between the crystals can at least be partly determined. Large crystals (*phenocrysts*) may be present in a groundmass of finer ones, giving a porphyritic texture, indicating slow initial crystallization, followed by more rapid cooling (No. 133). If the grain size is large enough, something of the sequence of crystallization may be discernible, earlier formed crystals having the more complete outlines, while later ones may partially or completely surround them. Much of this determination, however, has to be made by examination of thin sections using a microscope.

Other variations in texture are important clues to the mode of intrusion and cooling history of the rock. Layering or banding indicates either a frozen flowage of the magma, or settling of crystals in the magma chamber (No. 134). In the latter case the structures produced are analogous to those in a sediment: grading, lamination and even current bedding and erosion surfaces have been described. Much will depend on whether the magma was in motion while the crystals were settling out, and whether that motion was steady or intermittent. They are more commonly found in basic igneous rocks, perhaps reflecting their lower viscosity. Compositional as well as textural changes may occur in layered and other intrusions. As a magma cools, not all the minerals begin to crystallize out at once. The earlier crystals may sink to the floor of the magma chamber, while the remaining magma is thereby altered in composition. This gives rise to a chemical differentiation within the intrusion. In general, the earliest formed minerals (crystallizing at the highest temperatures) are the ferromagnesian minerals, while feldspar and quartz come last. As a result, the intrusion may have earlier formed more basic portions, and residual acid ones. Occasionally this can be seen within the limits of a single intrusive body (some sills are more basic just above the basal chilled margin), and the process has often been invoked to account for the differences between individual intrusions and extrusions in a suite of related igneous rocks.

Close to contacts with the country rocks the intrusions generally become finer grained, due to more rapid cooling, and compositional changes also occur. The igneous rock against the contact may represent the original composition of the magma, chilled and consolidated before any differentiation took place. Where the intrusion is discordant, the process of emplacement can also be observed, frozen in the now solid rock. This proceeds by *stoping*, the magma penetrating the country rock in a network of veins, causing it to break off into blocks (*xenoliths*), which become incorporated within the intrusion (No. 137). These xenoliths are highly thermally metamorphosed, and can even become completely melted, and assimilated within the magma.

During late stages of cooling, particularly of the large granitic plutons, veining of the cooling intrusion and the surrounding country rock, by the remaining liquids of the magma, may take place. *Aplite veins*, of a fine sugary intergrowth of quartz and feldspar, probably represent the residual magma, drained of all ferromagnesian minerals, and able to remain liquid at a lower temperature than the bulk of the intrusion. In complete contrast are the *pegmatites*, also containing quartz and feldspar, but with a variety of often rare minerals, and with extremely large crystals (No. 151). In this case the crystals probably formed from a watery magma, perhaps by precipitation as much as by solidification. Penetration of the country rock by such solutions is responsible for much of the mineralization surrounding large plutons.

Contact metamorphism in small scale intrusions is not severe, and may only extend a few centimetres from the contact. The degree of metamorphism will depend partly on the temperature of the magma at the time of intrusion, and partly on the amount of magma which has passed through. A comparatively thin dyke, if it was a channel for a large volume of magma (perhaps feeding a fissure eruption), will have a wider contact zone than a thicker dyke, which was not a major feeder.

Igneous Relationships

The igneous rocks of a particular episode of activity will generally fall into a pattern of both rock types and types of extrusion and intrusion. Central to this theme is the concept of a parental magma type, a melt of a particular chemical composition, at a considerable depth in most cases, which provided the source material for both intrusions and extrusions (if any). This melt may be basic (usually derived from beneath the continental crust), acidic (from the melting of continental crust during orogeny), or intermediate (the andesite found in island arc volcanoes). The composition of the igneous rocks found varies from this parental norm, due to either assimilation or melting of additional material, or to differentiation. In the latter case the ferromagnesian minerals and the calcic plagioclase settle out, leaving a residual liquid richer in sodic plagioclase, orthoclase and quartz. Given a basic parental magma, this process, with removal of the residual liquid, will produce both an ultrabasic rock (the solid phaze left behind), and a small proportion of granite. Thus in the Tertiary Igneous Province of northern Britain basic and acid rocks are found both as extrusions and intrusions.

The reconstruction of magma differentiation is a matter as much for the laboratory as the field. Accurate chemical analyses are necessary, including trace elements, while the details of mineral crystallization are observed under the microscope. Conversely the order of events, the relative chronology, is a matter of field observation.

The contact between an intrusion and either sedimentary or igneous rocks will usually leave no doubt that the igneous rock was injected as a magma; chilling of the intrusion against the contact and inclusion of xenoliths of country rock are the main evidence to look for. The same features are present when one igneous rock intrudes another, though if the earlier rock was still hot there may be little chilling of the later. Sometimes the contact looks like that between two immiscible liquids, and this may indeed have been the case (No. 138). Alternatively, the intruded rock may have been hot and plastic, but not molten. No. 138 also illustrates another feature, the interchange of molecules across the contact without its disruption, a process described as *diffusion*.

Within volcanic provinces, which must of course have intrusive rocks beneath, high level intrusions are often found intruded into the lavas and pyroclastic rocks. Feeder dykes and pipes may cut vertically through the extrusive rocks and any interbedded sediments, while horizontal or inclined sills may be interleaved with them.

1 Fresh water conglomerates

2 Breccio-conglomerate

3 Gash Breccia on limestone

4 Unconformity and breccia

5 Boulder beds above unconformity

6 Tight folding and unconformity

7 Irregular surface of unconformity

8 Glauconitic conglomerate

9 Phosphatic pebbles or nodules

10 Raised beach

11 Glacially striated surface

12 Chalky Boulder Clay

13 Solifluction terrace

14 Boulder Clay and Head

15 Carboniferous varved clays

16 A sequence of Head deposits

17 Push or staunch moraine

18 Angular unconformity

19 Dune bedded sandstones

20 Breccia with burrows

21 Quartzite

22 Sandstones and mudstones with oxidation/reduction colouration

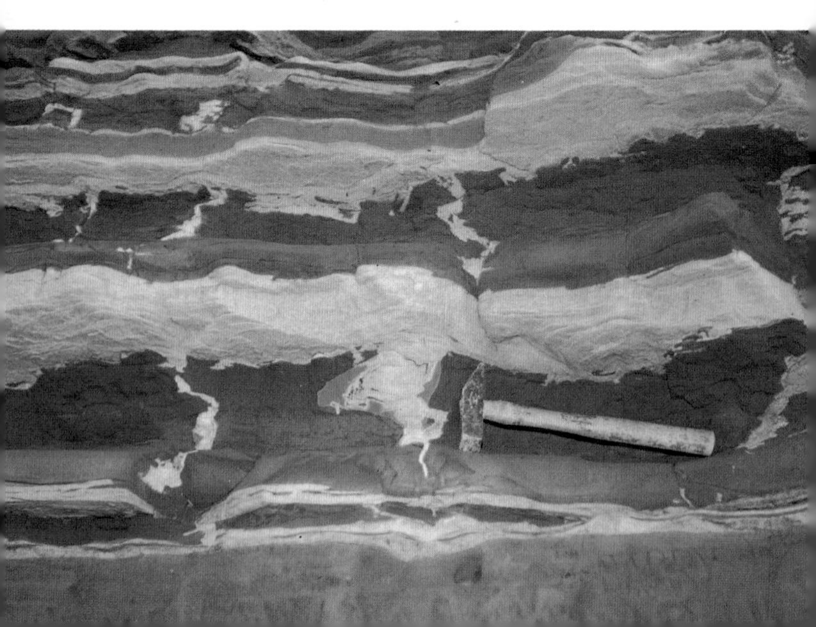

23 Ripple marks in shallow water sandstones

24 Sandstone pipes infilling potholes

25 Rain pits and footprints on sand surface

26 Ripple drift bedding in turbidites

27 Slight angular discordance between siltstones

28 Crinoidal shales, vertical section

29 Crinoidal shales, bedding plane

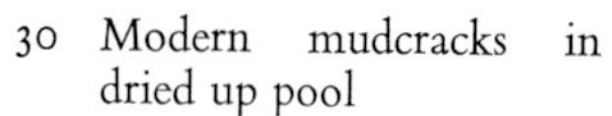

30 Modern mudcracks in dried up pool

31 Fossil mudcracks

32 Kimmeridge Clay with ammonites

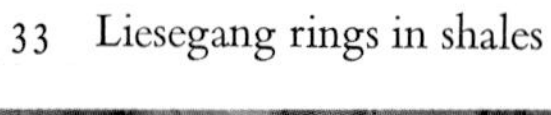

33 Liesegang rings in shales

34 Landslipping in clays

35 Repeated turbidites

36 Flute casts in turbidites

37 and 38 Slumped sediment in turbidites

39 Slumping due to loading

40 Convolute bedding and ripple marks in turbidites

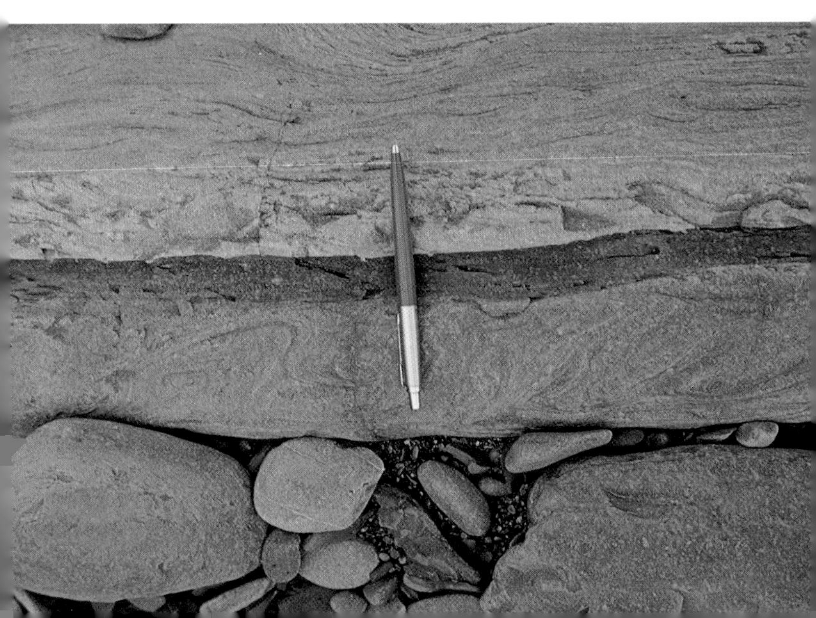

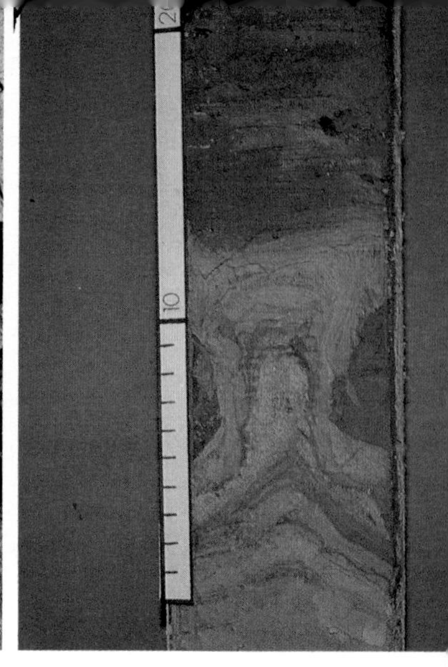

41 Neptunean dykes in turbidites

42 Diapiric structure in recent sediments

43 Intraformational clast in turbidite

44 Fossil patch reefs in limestone

45 Nodular limestones and shales

46 Modern coquina

47 Solution pipes in Chalk

48 Corals *in situ* on bedding plane

49 Ironstones and estuarine beds

50 Stylolitic surfaces in limestones

51 Concretionary limestone

52 Conformable limestones and shales

53 Collapse structures in limestones

54 Evaporites in marls

55 Brecciated Magnesian Limestone

56 Bone Bed

57 Coal seam with thrust faulting

58 Coal Measures and sandstones

59 Coaly shales, ironstones and sandstones

60 Seat earth with fossil plants

61 Concretion in shales

62 Cone-in-cone concretion in turbidite sequence

63 Flint in Chalk

64 Chert in dolomite

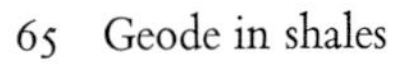

65 Geode in shales

66 Irregular burrow system in shales

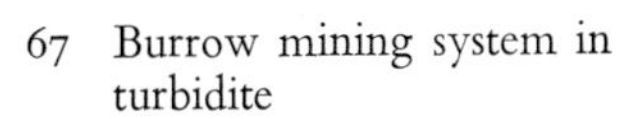

67 Burrow mining system in turbidite

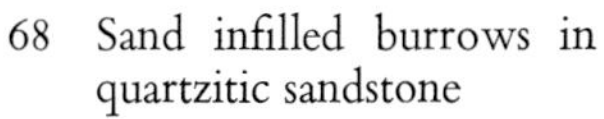

68 Sand infilled burrows in quartzitic sandstone

69 Trace fossils in limestone

70 Doubtful trace fossils

71 *Palaeodictyon* and other trace fossils in turbidite

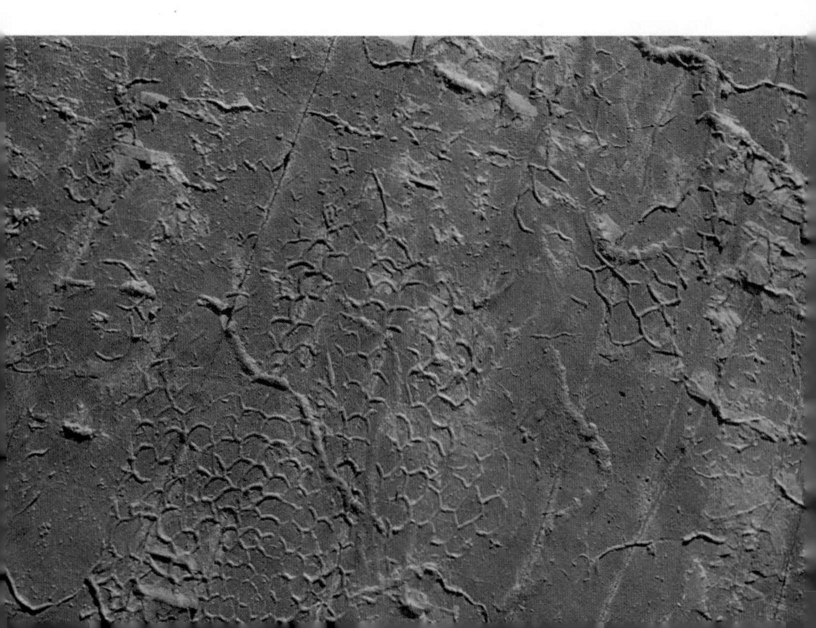

72 Faulted anticline and syncline

73 Bedding and slaty cleavage in shales

74 Post folding cleavage in syncline

75 Vertical strata

76 Faulted anticline and syncline in plan view

77 Conjugate folds

78 Bedding/cleavage relationship in 'right way-up' beds

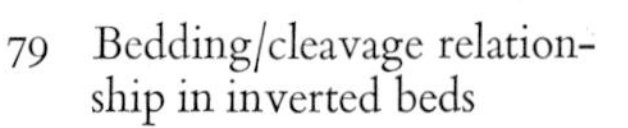

79 Bedding/cleavage relationship in inverted beds

80 Tectonic alignment of pebbles

81 Fracture cleavage in sandstones

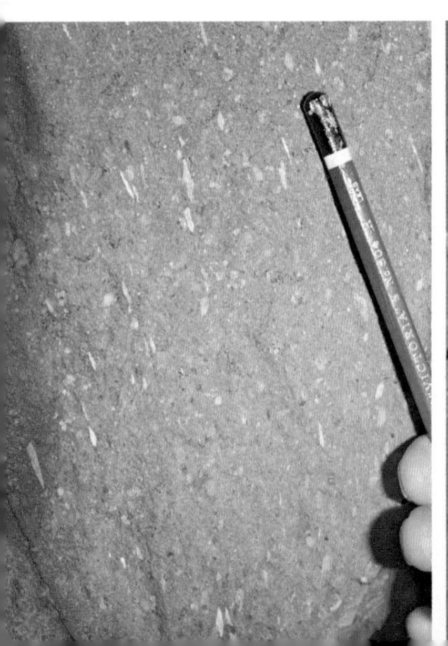

82 Minor folding on major fold limb

83 Isoclinal fold and thrust

84 Growth fibres and slickensides on a fault plane

85 Dolerite sill faulted against sandstones

86 Normal fault in shales

87 Low-angle fault in Chalk

88 Normal fault

89 Calcite and sediment infilling a vug

90 Small normal fault in limestones

91 Inclined fold and thrust in limestones

92 and 93 Folding and thrusting in Coal Measures

94 Low-angle thrust

95 Thrust plane cutting folded limestones

96 Conjugate fault sets in tuffs and shales

97 Conjugate tear faults in shales and sandstones

98 Fibrous quartz vein infilling a fault

99 Mineralized quartz vein

100 Tension gashes in sandstone

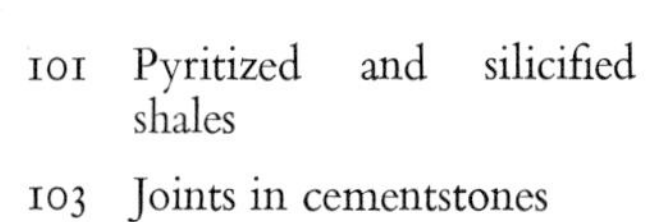

101 Pyritized and silicified shales

102 Ptygmatic folds in quartz veins

103 Joints in cementstones

104 Scarp in basalts and volcanic neck

105 Joint plane with feather fracture

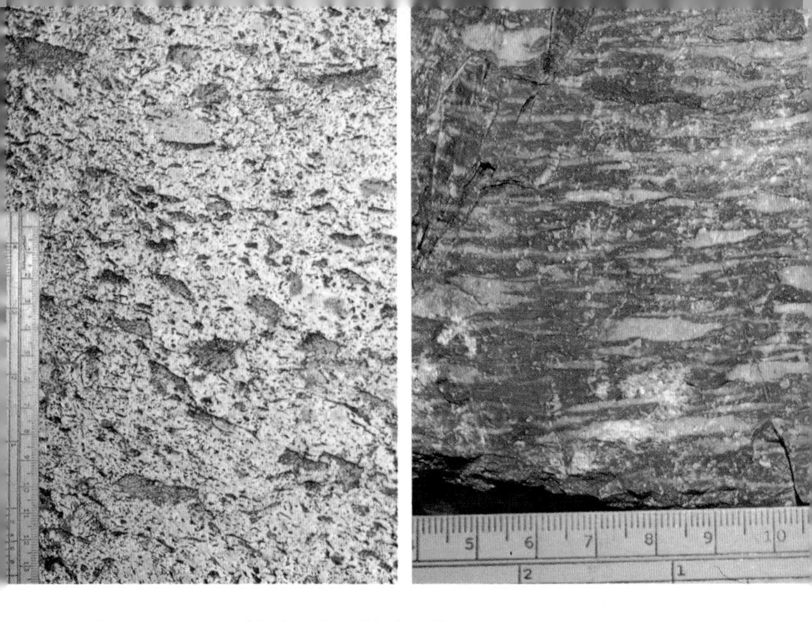

106 and 107 Non-welded and welded tuffs

108 Tuff dyke in limestones and shales

109 Bedded waterlain tuffs

110 Volcanic neck

111 Basaltic agglomerate

112 Dyke associated with volcanic neck of No. 110

113 Volcanic neck in rhyolite

114 Vertical section in basalts and laterite

115 Basalts resting on Chalk

116 Laterite and cinder bed beneath basalt flow

117 Spheroidal weathering in laterite

118 Columnar basalt

119 Pillow lavas

120 Pillow lavas with interstitial limestone

121 Jointing in granite

122 Flowfolds in pitchstone

123 Dolerite sill in sandstones

124 Close-up of contact in No. 123

125 Contact metamorphism at the top of a dolerite sill

126 Porcellanite with ammonites

127 Roof of granite sill

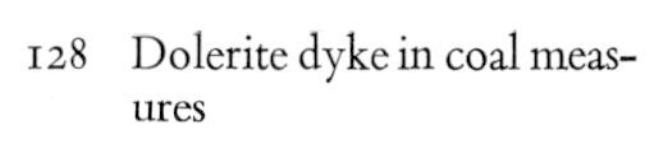

128 Dolerite dyke in coal measures

129 Granite dykes in slates

130 Basic dykes in gneiss

131 Cone sheets intruded into limestones

132 Granite cutting hornfels

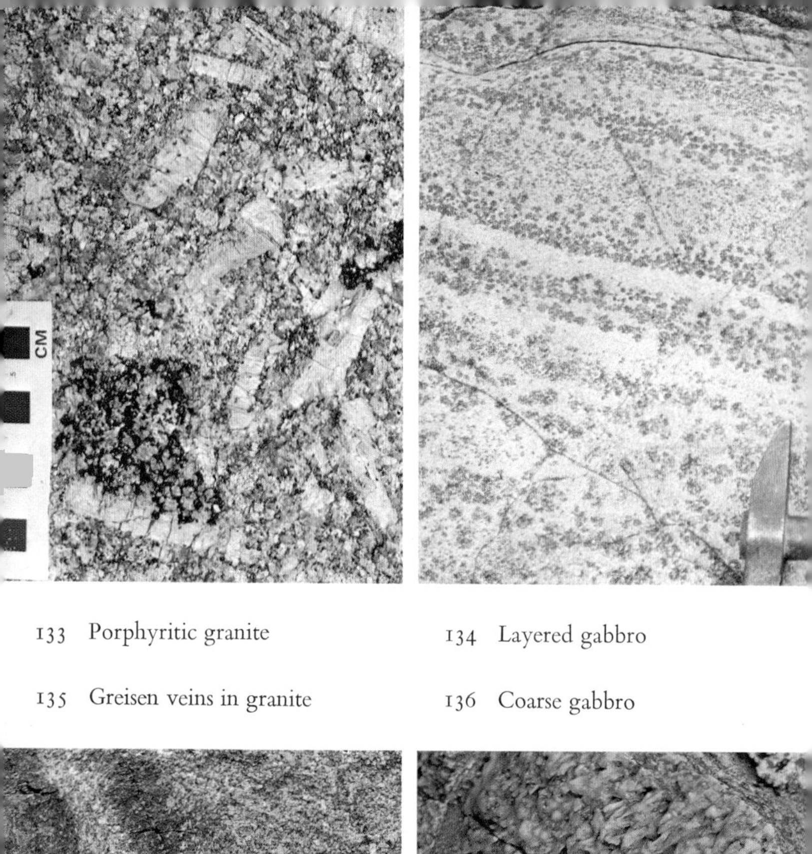

133 Porphyritic granite

134 Layered gabbro

135 Greisen veins in granite

136 Coarse gabbro

137 Intrusion breccia

138 Contact between igneous rocks

139 Folded phyllites

140 Syncline in low grade schists

141 Folded phyllites

142 Refolded psammitic bands in schists

143 Boudinaged quartz vein

144 Fold interference patterns in gneiss

145 Quartz-feldspar schist

146 Metamorphosed turbidites

147 Garnet mica schist

148 Banded migmatites

149 Migmatites

150 Migmatite

151 Pegmatite vein in gneiss

152 Dendritic marks in limestone

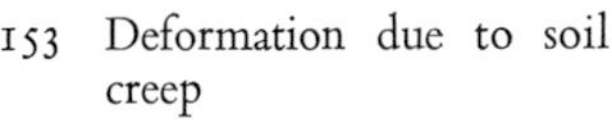

153 Deformation due to soil creep

154 and 155 Hand drilling or augering

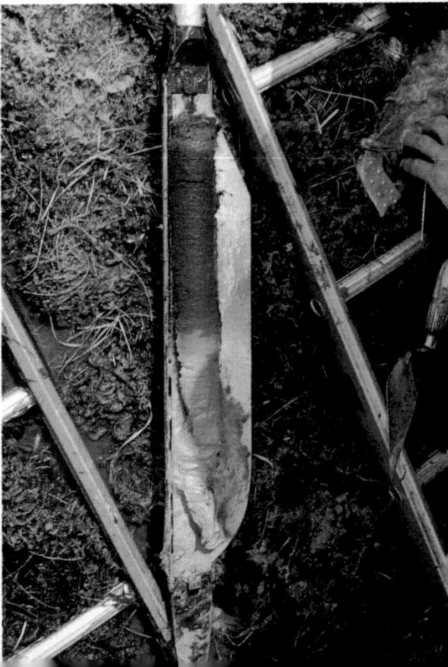

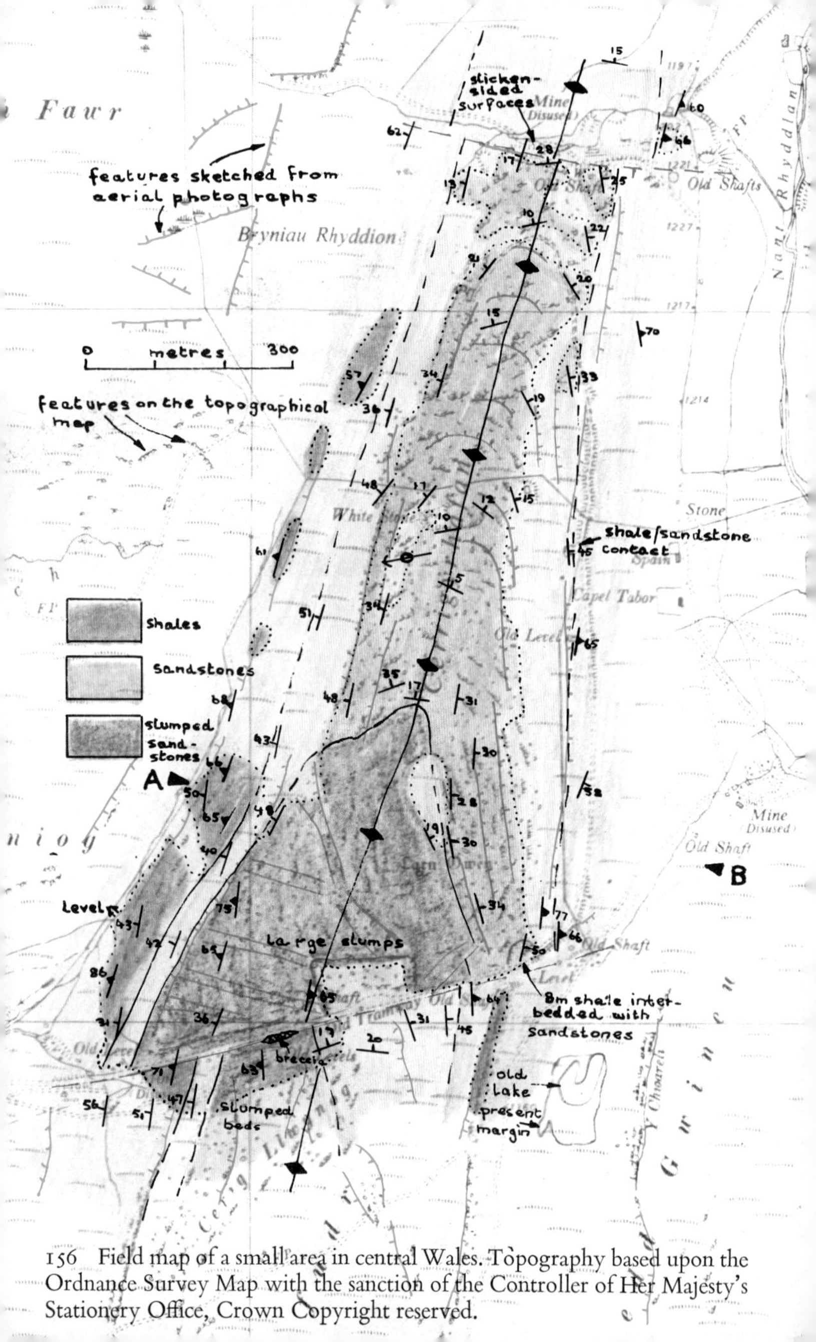

156 Field map of a small area in central Wales. Topography based upon the Ordnance Survey Map with the sanction of the Controller of Her Majesty's Stationery Office, Crown Copyright reserved.

6 METAMORPHIC ROCKS AND STRUCTURES

Metamorphic rocks have been altered, by recrystallization of their minerals, while still in a solid state, by heat (*thermal* or *contact metamorphism*), pressure (*dynamic metamorphism*) or both (*regional metamorphism* or metamorphism *sensu stricto*). Recrystallization of minerals may take place at any time after deposition of a sedimentary rock, but the diagenesis which takes place at low temperature and pressure, converting the sediment into a normal sedimentary rock, is excluded from metamorphic processes.

Thermal Metamorphism

Metamorphism by heat alone generally occurs where molten igneous material bakes the country rocks into or through which it is being injected. These rocks can be of any type, sedimentary, igneous or metamorphic. The degree of alteration depends on the temperature of the intruded material, and the size of the intrusion or amount of magma which flows past.

Recrystallization of mineral constituents may involve either change of a single mineral to a higher temperature form (e.g. quartz to tridymite or cristobalite) or more complicated recrystallization in which two or more minerals may react chemically, to produce new minerals. Quartz and calcite can react to form the mineral wollastonite, a lime silicate. Further reactions may take place between the country rock and the magma, or solutions emanating from it. In extreme cases the country rock may even melt, to be either mixed with the magma, or remain immiscible and crystallize as a separate rock.

Pure quartzites and limestones recrystallize to metaquartzites and marbles. Argillaceous rocks form more varied derivatives. At first the rock may be bleached, and the clay minerals recrystallize to chlorites. More severe baking produces a schistose rock, with at successively higher grades andalusite, cordierite and sillimanite forming conspicuous crystals, looking like porphyritic crystals in an igneous rock (No. 127). The rock may become hard and flinty, and is then termed a *hornfels* (Nos 126, 127, 132).

Dynamic Metamorphism

Metamorphism by pressure alone occurs principally in narrow belts along fault planes, where stress reaches a maximum. Heat is added by friction between the walls of the fault. Low angle reverse faults, or thrusts, are commonly associated with *mylonites*, literally milled rocks, formed by the grinding and crushing of the masses, with eventual recrystallization to produce a flinty rock.

Regional Metamorphism

In large scale tectonic activity, when great thicknesses of rock are strongly folded and deeply buried, both high stresses and temperatures are generated. Rock masses are strongly deformed mechanically, and also recrystallized, so that eventually material may actually melt to form magmas at great depth, which then migrate upwards to be emplaced as intrusions.

Metamorphic rocks cannot be observed in the making, but the process is normally envisaged as a progressive one: metamorphic rocks can be arranged in a series, showing increasing effects of metamorphism. As with thermal metamorphism, rocks of simple composition such as quartz sandstones and limestone, behave simply, recrystallizing to quartzites and marbles under comparatively low conditions of temperature and pressure. Sediments containing appreciable amounts of clay minerals, varied rock fragments, and igneous rocks, behave chemically in a much more complex manner. Sequences of appearance and replacement of metamorphic minerals, grown in the solid state, can be recognized. The best known is that which occurs in argillaceous rocks, in which the clay minerals successively recrystallize as chlorite, muscovite, biotite, garnet, kyanite and sillimanite. These minerals mark successive metamorphic grades, and are used as indicators of the severity of regional metamorphism.

As pressure and temperature pass their maximum and then wane, the rocks are in most cases 'frozen' at their maximum degree of metamorphism. In some cases however retrogressive metamorphism may occur, in which crystals of lower metamorphic grades partially or completely replace the higher grade minerals.

Together with recrystallization during metamorphism, mechanical deformation also affects the strata. Predominantly, this takes the form of folding, with subordinate thrusting. Metamorphic structures can be crudely described as plastic: the rock appears to have been relatively 'soft' and pliable. Indeed, metamorphic folds often resemble the folds which occur in slumping during deposition of sediments (compare No. 40 and No. 141). Well defined faults can generally be observed to cut the metamorphic folds and crystals, and belong to a later period when the rock was cooler and more brittle.

Cleaved and folded sediments, with no obvious recrystallization (Nos 73, 141) form the starting point for metamorphic rocks, as usually understood. Recrystallization commences in the finer layers, the clay minerals being altered to chlorite and then white mica or muscovite. The grain size is larger than in a typical slate. Deformation also progresses with tightening of the fold limbs, and often with transfer of material into the hinge zones and attenuation of the limbs. Rocks of this grade, in the finer grained sediments, are termed *phyllites*.

Schists are generated from phyllites, by further alteration including the appearance of mica flakes which are easily visible to the naked eye, of the order of 1–2mm across. Structural complexity is also greater, as hinge zones of folds, and limbs, become even more differentiated. Also the folds are often refolded (No. 142), producing complicated hook structures, and interference folds (No. 144). Destruction of the original sedimentary layering becomes evident at this stage in many exposures, as material is streaked out into the planes of foliation or schistosity, and quartz and other veins similarly injected. Consequently, in many schists and higher grade rocks, the original sedimentary layering is completely lost, at outcrop scale (No. 145).

Classification of schists is based principally on their mineralogy, which in turn is governed by the original composition of the rock. Basic igneous rocks, or pyroclastic or sedimentary rocks derived mainly from them, form *green-schists*, with chlorite and epidote as a dominant constituent. Feldspar may be present as an original constituent (in an arkose, or igneous rock) or may appear as a purely metamorphic mineral in rocks containing both clay minerals and quartz. Other schists with complex mineralogies result from the metamorphism of calcareous or siliceous (silty or sandy) mudstones, to give calcareous schists, and quartz or quartzo-feldspathic schists. In informal descriptions of rocks, the terms *pelite* (predominantly formed of platy minerals) and *psammite* (predominantly quartz) are often used.

Gneiss results from further increase in the metamorphic grade: a granular texture replaces the schistose one, and the structural complexity of the lower grade rocks is often simplified, by the obliteration of the earlier structures. The pressure is higher, particularly the hydrostatic pressure, and under these conditions the minerals tend to segregate into layers which bear no resemblance to the original banding, or perhaps even to an earlier cleavage or schistosity. Light quartzo-feldspathic layers alternate with darker micaceous bands, which may also contain hornblende, pyroxene and other minerals. The layers can be regular and parallel-sided, with folds which are hairpin-shaped in cross-section, much thickened in the hinge zone. *Augen-gneiss* is a distinct variety, in which large crystals have the foliation wrapped or deflected round them, to give each crystal the appearance of an eye.

In the highest grade rock bands of granitic composition may alternate with more basic bands, giving the appearance of layers of acid and basic igneous rock. It may be difficult to decide whether either, or both types of band may have become molten: we may be close to the origin of some igneous rocks. Acid material may appear to have been injected in sheets between more basic layers (No. 148), forming mixed rocks, the *migmatites*. Finally, definite melting and mobilization of the acid material may be indicated by cross-cutting veins with sharp contacts (Nos 149, 150). The great granite batholiths of some orogenic belts may have originated in this way, by wholesale movement of the acid portion of a migmatite, leaving the basic portions beneath.

7 THE WEATHERING OF ROCKS

The majority of pictures in the colour section are of fresh exposures of rock, where the surface is clean cut, often polished, and the original features of the rock can be clearly seen. In contrast, particularly in mapping, the geologist will have to deal with exposures which are much less than ideal in this respect, in which superficial effects will have occurred, both physical and chemical, which can mislead the unwary.

Physical effects are primarily due to gravity, and occur mainly on hill slopes. *Soil creep* or *terminal curvature* is the most difficult effect to recognize, but it is very common where conditions are right (No. 153). It is caused by the gradual downslope movement of the soil cover. Larger scale movement of rock, such as landslipping (Fig. 5, No. 34) is much easier to detect, and gives rise to distinctive topographic features. Development of some types of joints (pp. 73, 193) is thought to be another effect of the removal of overburden and weathering.

Chemical weathering takes place particularly under a cover of moist soil, within which water movement is slow, giving ample time for chemical breakdown of the rock (in contrast it is not a major phenomenon on shores or in fast flowing streams, where mechanical removal of rock is much more important). One should look for signs of chemical weathering in small outcrops in regions of thick soil cover, and in artificial exposures such as the upper parts of quarry faces. Under these conditions the silicate minerals tend to break down to oxides and soluble carbonates, and weathering proceeds inwards from planes of easy access for water, such as joint and bedding planes. Cores of relatively unweathered rock are left, rounded off in contrast to the angular blocks delimited by the cracks (*spheroidal weathering*).

The most common oxide is the brown iron oxide, limonite, which imparts a brown colour, sometimes with iridescent colouring, to a wide variety of rocks (Nos 49, 58, 59). It may both permeate the rock and also form stains on bedding and joint planes. The removal of lime from calcareous sandstones, siltstones and shales may change the rock from a grey colour, with shells present, to a crumbly or *friable* brown rottenstones, containing only shell impressions.

Dendritic markings (No. 152) are caused by ground water incompletely penetrating bedding planes and joints, etc., under capillary action. The mineral stains thus deposited are often tree-like in shape and can be mistaken for fossil remains.

Liesegang rings (No. 33) are formed by water similarly permeating the rock, but depositing material in roughly parallel shells inwards from the joint and bedding planes. These rings can easily be mistaken for bedding planes, particularly if seen in a small exposure. Sometimes they give the effect of current bedding, which may be sufficiently convincing to deceive even an experienced geologist. Similar banding is sometimes found in concretions, and can also be mistaken for bedding.

Weathering effects of these types should also be looked for within geological sequences, as *fossil weathering*, particularly beneath unconformities. The red colour of the shales in No. 33 is a good example of this, though the Liesegang rings are probably of later origin. The fossil weathering of the basalts at the Giant's Causeway (Nos 114–8) contrasts with modern weathering there to a brown soil.

III COLOUR PLATE DESCRIPTIONS

The colour plates are grouped in an order (Nos 1 to 156) which generally follows that of the preceding chapters of this book: sedimentary rock types are dealt with first and are followed by simple tectonic structures (note that most of the illustrations of unconformities are near the beginning of the colour section, though the text dealing with them is relatively later). It will, however, be evident that many photographs show more than one geological feature; that of a fold will also illustrate at least one rock type, and an unconformity may bring together two distinct lithologies. Cross references are therefore given where it is felt they are useful.

The text describing each photograph is not purely a field description, in the form in which it would be recorded in a field notebook. Additional interpretation is given where apposite, and in some cases more information, not seen in the photograph, is added. Most illustrations are of 'outcrop size', and represent the view a geologist would have, and hence the detail he will see in the field. A variety of objects appears in the photographs, to illustrate scale, most commonly a geological hammer or a 'cm' scale. In most cases an exact scale is not needed, unless measurements are to be taken from the picture, and a rough indication will suffice, as the phenomena can be quite variable in size.

(*Note:* Throughout the text, colour plates are referred to as No. 1, Nos 3 and 4, etc., and line illustrations within the text appear as Fig. 1, etc.)

No. 1 **Conglomerate. Old Red Sandstone (Devonian).** *Cushendun, Co. Antrim, N. Ireland.*
Hundreds of feet of this conglomerate are present at this locality, and others in the Old Red Sandstone of northern Britain. Rounded boulders of quartzite, schist, granite and other igneous rocks, and some sandstones, are set in a matrix of red sandstone. Bedding is not obvious, except where sandstone bands are present. Two bands can be seen here, both above the hammer; they are impersistent laterally, and have abrupt contacts with the conglomerate. The upper surface of the lower sandstone is a good example of an *erosion surface*, eroded into the sandstones before deposition of the succeeding conglomerate. These conglomerates are succeeded in this area by non-marine river and flood plain deposits: this suggests that the conglomerates are also non-marine, and were deposited by torrents in a rugged landscape.

No. 2 **Polygenetic Breccio-conglomerate.** *La Tête des Hougues, Jersey, Channel Islands.*

A spectacular breccio-conglomerate containing cobbles and pebbles of a variety of rock-types, ranging in shape from very well rounded to markedly angular. The pinkish and purplish clasts are volcanic, the greyer ones of sedimentary origin, whilst some coarser textured granitic rocks are also present. Such a poorly-bedded, ill-sorted accumulation must have been produced by sheet floods sweeping across an irregular topography and depositing their load in a depression.

This Rozel Conglomerate is completely unfossiliferous, so it has been referred by different geologists to the younger Pre-Cambrian, to the Cambrian and to the New Red Sandstone.

No. 3 **Gash Breccia in Carboniferous Limestone.** *Lydstep near Tenby, Dyfed (Pembrokeshire), Wales.*

Massively bedded Carboniferous Limestone dipping vertically is overlain by a breccia of angular fragments of similar limestone set in a reddish matrix. Prominent joints in the limestone, some infilled with white calcite, dip to the left at about 45°. Further up the hillside more limestone outcrops can be seen. The 'gash breccias' infill large irregularly shaped holes in the limestone. The exposure is on the margin of one of these.

They are interpreted as having been formed by the collapse of caves which had been eroded into the limestone. When the walls and the roofs of the caves collapsed, they carried down with them overlying reddish sediments of Triassic age. Erosion has stripped these Triassic beds off the present surface of the limestone, so they are only preserved in the 'gash breccias'.

No. 4 **Angular unconformity. Permian breccias on Devonian slates.** *Waterside Cove, Paignton, Devonshire, England.*

Devonian slates and sandstones dip to the right (east); they are overlain by a distinctive breccia, formed of limestone blocks in a red matrix. This also dips to the east, but at a lower angle, clearly showing the discordance between the two systems. Note that the blocks in the breccia are not derived from the underlying beds, but come from limestones of Devonian age, exposed not far away.

No. 5 **Unconformity with spectacular basement conglomerate. Upper Cretaceous limestones resting on metamorphic rocks of Pre-Cambrian age.** *Kank Hill near Kutná Hora, Czechoslovakia.*

The brown rocks in the lower part of the exposure are vertical Pre-Cambrian metamorphics, as can be seen from the colour banding by the geologist's right elbow. On either side of his head, the very irregular upper surface of the metamorphics is clearly visible. The basal few feet of the overlying Cretaceous beds is a conglomerate made up of rounded water worn fragments of the metamorphics ranging up into boulders a metre or more in diameter. This basal conglomerate passes up into the better bedded white detrital limestones of the top left hand corner of the exposure. These detrital limestones contain broken fragments of fossils that lived in extremely shallow water, whilst the upper surfaces of the larger boulders are encrusted with oysters, bryozoans and the tubes of serpulid worms. This quarry exposes the beach deposits and shelly sands laid down by the Cretaceous seas as they submerged a rocky coast line cut into the Pre-Cambrian metamorphics. Fossil beach deposits of this type are rarely to be found.

No. 6 **Tight folding and unconformity. Late Pre-Cambrian Malmesbury Group overlain by Silurian Table Mountain Group.** *Waaihoek, Cape Province, South Africa.*

Quartzites of the older series define tight, inclined folds: two anticlines and a central syncline can be made out, with softer shales in the core of the syncline. In the background the gently dipping Table Mountain Group cuts cleanly across the folds of the older system.

No. 7 **Irregular surface of unconformity. Lower Ordovician grits and conglomerates on pre-Cambrian quartzites.** *Ogof Gynfor, Anglesey, Wales.*

The older rocks are quartzites, with well defined bedding planes, dipping to the west (right). The surface of unconformity is irregular, with the Ordovician grits filling up the hollows. A prominent bed, about 2m up from the junction, contains quartzite blocks derived from older rocks. Note that the orange colour present on the rocks is caused by the growth of lichen.

Nos 8 and 9 **Unconformity. Upper Cretaceous chalk overlying Lias clays.** *Whitepark Bay, County Antrim, N. Ireland.*

Soft dark Lias clays form the older strata; they split along the bedding planes, and are therefore technically shales. The overlying rocks are a highly distinctive facies at the base of the Irish chalk. It is an unusual basal conglomerate, with a matrix of chalk. The grey colour of the basal chalk is due to dark green specks of the mineral glauconite (a hydrated silicate of iron, aluminium and potassium) which can form on the seafloor by the breakdown of igneous minerals such as biotite. Dark to light brown pebbles of phosphate are concentrated near the surface of unconformity. They may have been formed by either chemical growth *in situ*, as fossilized droppings from sea animals, or have been secondarily derived from older rocks by erosion and No. 9 shows some of these pebbles. That on the lower right has the form of the interior of one chamber of an ammonite shell: it strongly suggests that the pebble originated as a chemical precipitation within the shell, and following erosion of the shell from older strata, has been incorporated in the basal conglomerate. The conglomerate also contains broken pieces of the bivalve *Inoceramus*, seen here in cross-section as straight or slightly curved white bands.

Note that the surface of the unconformity is not regular, and that some of the younger beds even seem to be enclosed within the Lias clay. However, this is a two-dimensional cross-section, and the chalk is probably filling up an eroded hollow in the Lias.

No. 10 **Raised beach.** *Hope's Nose, Torquay, Devonshire, England.*

This raised beach, its base about 8m above sea level, is very well preserved; it is out of reach of the storm waves below, and is also extremely well indurated, by deposition of a lime cement between the sand grains and pebbles. Note the local limestone boulders at its base, derived from the Devonian limestones below. This particular locality is rich in mollusc shells, including oysters and mussels. The beach is 125,000 years old, and was produced during the last interglacial period, at a time of higher sea level following extensive melting of the ice sheets.

No. 11 **Glacial Striations on Carboniferous Limestones.** *Moelfre, Anglesey, Wales.*

Glacial striations are scratches found on smoothed outcrop surfaces formed by the abrasive action of ice sheets. Many of the scratches are cut by pebbles embedded in the base of the ice. As surface features of the rock, they will be preserved best when the rock is hard, or has been protected until recently by soil or boulder clay, or the ice has only recently retreated.

The surface is exposed at the top of solid rock sea-cliffs, in the soft Carboniferous Limestone, but has been protected until recently by the boulder clay seen to the top left. Hence the striations are fresh. They are also variable in direction. The boulder clay, left when the ice sheet melted, has a mixture of unconsolidated dark clay, now drying out, and blocks of a wide variety of rocks, some angular, some with rounded outlines.

No. 12 **Boulder Clay.** *Dimlington, Holderness, Humberside, England.*

Only ice could have transported and then deposited such a mixed deposit. In a matrix of dark clay containing fossils of Jurassic age, are erratic pebbles of a variety of Palaeozoic rocks and an abundance of white chalk ranging in size from pebbles down to pellets. The soft chalk could only have been transported in the frozen state.

This is a fresh unweathered exposure in typical Chalky Boulder Clay. On weathering the chalk will be dissolved away, the clays will oxidize to shades of brown, but the insoluble erratics will remain as evidence of glacial origin.

No. 13 **Solifluction terrace.** *Marros Sands, Carmarthen Bay, Dyfed (Carmarthenshire), Wales.*

The exposure is of soliflucted deposits of local material mantling a former sea cliff. The angular and sub-angular blocks tend to be aligned parallel to the solifluction movement. A polygonal system of ice cracks is exposed both in plan and section, infilled by blue to grey clay, and occasional blocks. The low cliff is topped by a thin soil, modified by farming operations.

No 14 **Boulder clay and Head.** *Newtown, Waterford, Eire.*

The Pleistocene deposits rest on a wavecut platform of Lower Palaeozoic rocks, exhumed in the foreground. Resting on this is a cryoturbated head of tabular blocks, many of them vertical in attitude. At the top of this layer is a brown *regolith*, or residual soil, developed on this surface before the deposition of the succeeding light coloured boulder clay. Both the head, and the boulder clay are thought to have been deposited during the last glaciation, the former during a period of cold climate (periglacial) which preceded the advance of the ice.

No. 15 **Varved clays. Gondwana Series, Carboniferous.** *North of São Paulo, Brazil.*

These varved lake clays come from the Permo-Carboniferous glaciation of South America, South Africa, India and Australia, produced as a polar icecap when these continents were fused together as Gondwanaland, which then lay over the South Pole (Fig. 21).

The clays show a seasonal rhythm, thin dark clays alternating with paler and thicker clays, siltstones and sandstones. In winter, when the lake may have been frozen, and also the rivers leading into it, the thin laminae of dark clay were deposited from suspension. Deposition of the pale beds took place during the rest of the year, when sediment was being fed from meltwaters. Most of this was probably also carried in suspension, since there is virtually no evidence in most beds of cross bedding, ripple marks, or other evidence of bottom currents; in contrast, even and continuous laminae make up these layers as well as the thin winter ones. A much thicker layer at the level of the hammer contrasts with these; it is coarser and thicker, with foreset bedding inclined to the left, and some evidence of ripple marks towards its top. From the evidence of all these annual cycles, or *varves*, one may surmise that these sediments were laid down in deep water, well away from any of the rivers entering the lake and from the deltaic deposits which they may have left.

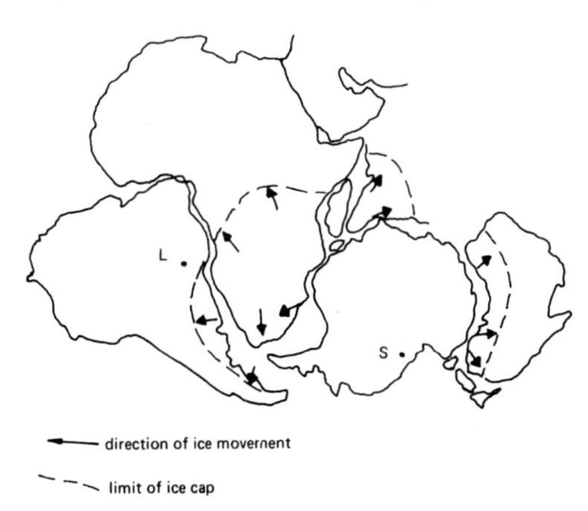

Fig. 21. *Reconstruction of Gondwanaland during the Upper Palaeozoic.* S: *Carboniferous South Pole.* L: *Location of No. 15.*

The boulder in the upper part of the succession is a glacial dropstone, carried by floating ice from which it fell as the ice melted. Floating ice may well have been a rare occurrence in this lake, as only this one boulder occurs in the forty annual cycles seen in the photograph.

These sediments are completely undeformed, apart from compaction (whose effects can be seen above the dropstone). They were laid down on the stable continental crust of South America, in a region which has since been unaffected by folding.

No. 16 **Head deposits.** *Marros Sands, Carmarthen Bay, Dyfed (Carmarthenshire), Wales.*

A sequence of deposits can be observed in this exposure:

3. Brown-yellow coloured head, with light bands due to frost cracks.
2. Coarse head with aligned sandstone blocks.
1. Head of fine shale fragments carrying a small number of blocks.

At the base is the modern pebble beach.

No. 17 **Push or staunch moraine.** *Bride moraine, Isle of Man, Great Britain.*

To the right (north) are sands and gravels, deposited as outwash from the ice sheet which covered the Irish Sea and the Isle of Man during the last glaciation (Devensian). They rest on boulder clay (behind the figures in the left-hand foreground), also of the last glaciation. To the top left is more of this boulder clay, which has been reverse faulted over the sands and gravels during a late readvance of the ice sheet, before it finally melted. The ice pushed the sands and gravels southwards and downwards, to give the reverse fault relationship seen here.

No. 18 **Angular unconformity. Middle Jurassic limestones resting on Carboniferous Limestone.** *Vallis Vale, Frome, Somerset, England.*

The lower part of the exposure shows dark coloured thick-bedded Carboniferous Limestone dipping to the left at about 30° (Fig. 22). These beds are overlain by flat lying yellowish oolitic limestones of Jurassic age. The three geologists are standing on the erosion surface that was cut across the Carboniferous Limestone. They are examining its features; its levelness, the clusters of oysters clamped on to it and the numerous burrows of several different sizes that penetrate down into the Carboniferous Limestone and are infilled with the yellow Jurassic sediments.

Fig. 22. *Unconformity at Vallis Vale (No. 18).*

No. 19 **Dune bedding. Navajo Sandstone, Jurassic.** *Capitol Reef, Utah, U.S.A.*

Both the large scale and the distinctive nature of aeolian dune bedding are well shown in this photograph of a cliff face, some 20m across. It is extremely rare to find perfectly horizontal, or flat bedding planes, and hence difficult to estimate accurately the strike and dip of the sandstones. Each unit here has the same sense of deposition, from right to left, recording the migration of the dunes, and the prevailing wind direction.

No. 20 **Fossil burrows. New Red Sandstone (Permo-Triassic).**

Goodrington near Paignton, Devonshire, England.

The New Red Sandstone is extremely ill-graded and contains sharp angular whitish and greyish clasts. To the right of the knife are two burrows with clear-cut walls and infilled with finer material. This infill shows a curved packing, parallel to the bottom of the right-hand burrow. The burrows are circular in cross section.

The New Red Sandstone of Devonshire was laid down on a land surface under hot arid or semi-arid conditions. Snakes and lizards, including the 'worm lizards' live in modern deserts, particularly on the margins. It has, therefore, been suggested that these particular burrows were made by a primitive reptile, using its heavily armoured head to force its way through the gravel and packing this behind with its stumpy tail.

No. 21 **Quartzite with current bedding and trace fossils. Pipe Rock, Lower Cambrian.** *Loch Kishorn, Ross & Cromarty, Scotland.*

The Pipe Rock is an almost pure quartzite, characterized by closely packed vertical animal burrows. It was deposited in shallow water, in a succession of sheets of sediment each about 30cm thick. Current bedding can be detected at some localities, but in most outcrops the original bedding has been completely destroyed by the activities of the burrowers. In this outcrop the burrows are unusually sparse, and foreset bedding can be seen in the upper bed, dipping to the right, traversed by a few vertical pipes. They were probably made by a burrowing worm, similar to the modern lugworm, *Arenicola.*

Along parts of the Moine Thrust Belt of north-west Scotland, the Pipe Rock has been inverted during the thrusting. Over a hundred years ago this was recognized by Nicol, who observed that the pipes opened downwards in some localities.

No. 22 **Sandstones and Mudstones with oxidation/reduction colouration. Triassic sandstones.** *Paignton, Devonshire, England.*

Green sandstones and red mudstones dip gently away from the observer, each mudstone layer having within it a series of mudcracks, each of which the succeeding sandstone has infilled. The green colouration is caused by the presence of iron oxide in its reduced state (FeO), while the red colour in the mudstones is due to the more completely oxidized iron ore (Fe_2O_3). The green zones are not strictly confined to the sandstones, but have an irregular contact within the mudstones, implying a post-depositional oxidation/reduction reaction in the iron content.

No. 23 **Ripple marks in shallow water sandstones. Grès Americain, Lower Ordovician.** *Camaret, Presqu'île de Crozon, Brittany, France.*

Shallow water sandstones dip steeply towards the observer, two bedding planes being exposed, separated by an oblique plane. The stratigraphically lower, to the left, has an unusual set of curved ripple marks – their asymmetry indicates that the current flowed from a point just off the outcrop to the upper left. This may have been the mouth of a constricted channel, from which the water flow fanned out. The upper bedding plane bears more normal parallel ripple marks, the current flowing approximately down dip.

No. 24 **Sandstone pipes. Lower Carboniferous.** *Trwyn Dwlban, Anglesey, Wales.*

A massive limestone crops out on the foreshore, with almost horizontal bedding. It is followed by two sandstones, which infill potholes in the limestone. The cross-section (Fig. 23) shows a reconstruction of the outcrop. The earlier potholes were filled with a sandstone bearing scattered quartz pebbles, which also persists as a thin skin on the limestone surface. A second generation of potholes was then drilled, cutting indiscriminately through the limestone and the earlier potholes, the infill of which must have been already cemented. These second potholes were infilled by a finer, nonpebbly sandstone, which also (outside the limits of the photograph), overlies the earlier sandstone, and is succeeded by shales. Thus a series of events can be inferred from the cross-cutting relationships of the different beds: deposition and lithification of limestone, drilling of potholes, infilling by pebbly sand, lithification of sand to sandstone, drilling of more potholes, infilling by fine sand, and deposition of mud. Correspondingly, a sequence of changing environments can be reconstructed, involving repeated erosion and possible uplift.

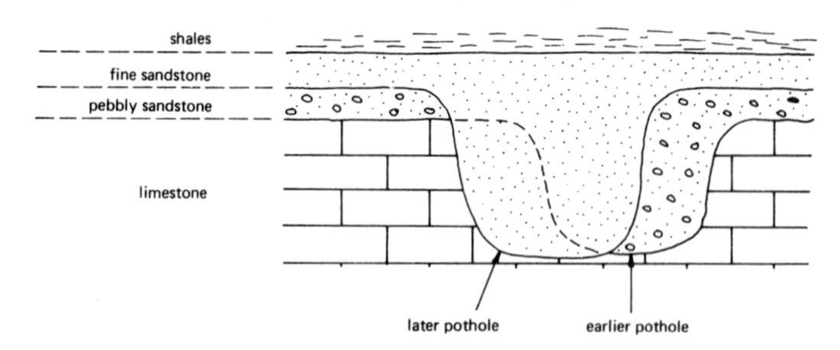

Fig. 23. *Cross section through the potholes of No. 24.*

No. 25 Rain-pits and footprints. *Modern beach surface, Brittany, France.*

Impressions of this type are occasionally preserved in very shallow water sandstones, and are conclusive evidence of emergence of the sand flats during deposition (though footprints can be formed under very shallow water). Rain drops falling at an angle to the vertical, will produce elliptical pits, deeper at one end, and hence the 'palaeo-wind' can be deduced. Fossil footprints can also be used to tell us something about the animal responsible: its size and gait, the number of legs, and even perhaps something of its behaviour!

Vague linear markings, running away from the camera, were caused by water movement, during the last tide. Like the other markings, they can be preserved in fossil form.

No. 26 Ripple-drift bedding. Aberystwyth Grits, Lower Silurian. *Clarach, Dyfed (Cardiganshire), Wales.*

These ripple marks, seen in section, illustrate both lateral and vertical deposition of fine sand and silt. Deposition took place on both the lee slope and the upstream or *stoss* slope, with thickening of each lamina of sediment on the lee slope, where current velocity was lower. Each ripple crest migrated down current (to the left), and also migrated or climbed higher. A thin layer of parallel laminae succeeded, grading up into shales with the settling out of the remaining silt.

Although here seen within a turbidite sequence, deposited in deep water, similar sedimentary structures may be found in shallow water sediment.

No. 27 Slight angular discordance between beds of Lower Silurian and Upper Ordovician age. *Onny River near Wistanstow, Salop, England.*

At first glance this river bank exposure would seem to show a conformable succession of shales and thin-bedded siltstones, but closer inspection shows that the geologist is examining an upper unit dipping gently towards his right. Beneath his feet, and best seen in the bottom left hand corner, beds of very similar lithology dip to the right at a slightly higher angle. Notice the angular discordance between the groups of beds above and below the hammer. The fossils that can be collected from the two groups of beds show that there is a considerable time gap between the two units, whilst when the basal Silurian rocks are traced for a few miles along the valley of the River Onny, they are found to overstep across various horizons of the Ordovician succession with the angular discordance at their base becoming more pronounced.

Unfortunately geologists collecting from the exposure shown have caused so much damage to the river bank that the land owner will no longer give permission to visit it.

Nos 28 and 29 Carboniferous shales. *Bundoran, Co. Sligo, Eire.*

These shales are well laminated, but also tend to split along planes slightly oblique to the bedding, a characteristic of many fine grained rocks. Very thin limestone beds are also present. Crinoid stem ossicles are the principal fossils seen, forming short pieces of stem lying in the plane of the bedding, or individual ossicles lying like coins on the surface. Many of these pieces of stem have been partly or completely crushed flat. The bedding plane shows a polygonal system of cracks breaking up the shale into pieces each about 1 cm in diameter. These are probably shrinkage cracks developed during the weathering of the shale in outcrop, rather than any mud-cracking in Carboniferous times.

No. 30 **Modern mudcracks.** *Quarry floor, Warboys, Cambridgeshire, England.*

Silt deposited in a pond is overlain by a thin veneer of fine mud. Following drying up of the pond, the sediment has shrunk on exposure to air and sunlight with the opening of a roughly polygonal series of fissures, *suncracks* or *mudcracks*. Additionally, the topmost mud veneer is curling up and parting from the underlying silt. The upper surface of these flakes is rain pitted, giving a mottled texture.

If this surface were to be drowned and subsequently buried beneath further sediment, the mudflakes might be carried off to be deposited elsewhere, or broken up, while sediment would infill the mudcracks (cf. No. 22). Infilled mudcracks can thus be used both as an indicator of very shallow water, with intermittent drying up, and also as a way-up indicator in strongly folded strata.

No. 31 **Fossil mudcracks. Juniata Formation. Upper Ordovician.** *Joppa, Tennessee, U.S.A.*

The mudcracks shown are in fine sediment deposited on the flats of an ancient delta. Erosion has weathered out the sediment infilling the cracks, which have been infilled with moss.

No. 32 **Kimmeridge Clay. Upper Jurassic.** *Kimmeridge, Dorset, England.*

This dark grey and only partially consolidated clay is typical of many of the Mesozoic clays of England. It is not quite consolidated enough to be termed either a shale or mudstone. There has, however, been considerable compaction, causing the thin-shelled ammonites to be flattened and broken. Otherwise, the shells are relatively unaltered, as is indicated by the mother-of-pearl lustre which they still retain.

No. 33 **Liesegang Rings. Late Pre-Cambrian shales.** *Coast west of Telgruc, Presqu'île de Crozon, Brittany, France.*

The bedding planes in the shales run across the photograph, including a few graded siltstones, showing the direction of younging of the sediment. At this coastal exposure these low-grade metamorphic rocks are overlain by red Ordovician conglomerates, and a reddened zone is present in the older rocks to a depth of some 10 m below the plane of the unconformity. The relatively more oxidized (red) and less oxidized (green) banding caused during this phase of weathering is parallel to the original bedding. The Liesegang rings, which are related to both bedding and to prominent joints, are later than this period of pre-Ordovician reddening, and cut completely across the reduced bands and patches (Fig. 24).

The sequence of events deduced from this exposure was probably as follows:

1. Deposition of shales.
2. Folding and slight metamorphism.
3. Erosion to the plane of unconformity.
4. Deposition of Ordovician basal conglomerate, with reddening of the older rocks.
5. Folding of the Ordovician, and formation of joints.
6. Weathering, and production of the Liesegang rings.

No. 34 **Landslipping.** *Black Ven between Charmouth and Lyme Regis, Dorset, England.*

The horizontal yellow sands and sandstones of the Upper Greensand (Upper Cretaceous) rest with slight unconformity on the gently eastward dipping greyish and drab coloured clays of the Lower Lias (Lower Jurassic). Water percolating through the sands is held up at the sand/clay junction, lubricating it to produce collapse and land slipping. Above Black Ven (the black bog) used to run, near the skyline of the photograph, the coast road linking Charmouth and Lyme Regis. In 1924 this road was broken by a land slip and by 1927 it was impassable even on foot. Landslipping is still taking place. The

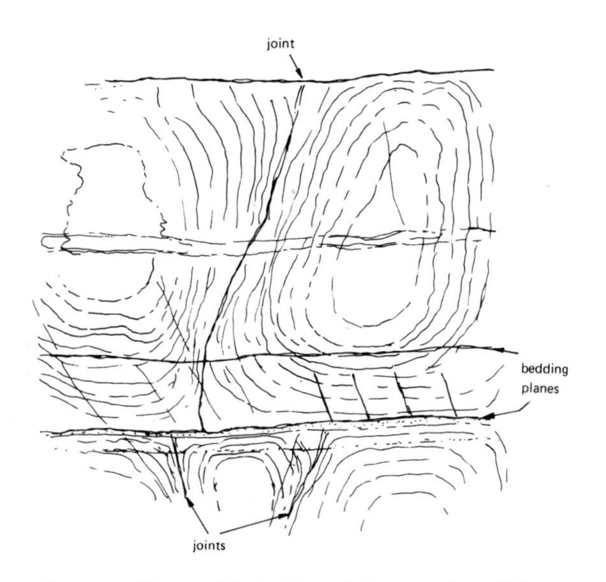

Fig. 24. *Close-up of the bedding and Liesegang rings of No. 33.*

fresh faces of yellow sand or of the clays mark the back of successive slips. At the foot of each of these scarps is a strip of boggy ground, difficult, indeed dangerous, to cross especially after heavy rain. Each of the slipped blocks is tilted northwards (landwards). Fragments of chert and hard sandstone from the Cretaceous rocks are strewn all over the foundered ground. They are carried seawards by the landslipping until they reach the modern beach. Wave attack weakens the toe of the slipped area and helps to cause further movement.

No. 35 **Repeated turbidites. Aberystwyth Grits, Lower Silurian.** *Aberystwyth, Dyfed (Cardiganshire), Wales.*

The successive beds of siltstones and sandstones of each turbidite unit each start with a sharp base on the underlying shale, and show laminations either throughout, or towards the top, where there is a gradual passage into the succeeding grey shale. The fining or *grading* upwards of the turbidites is particularly obvious in the thicker units (A and E, Fig. 25), but can also be detected with care in

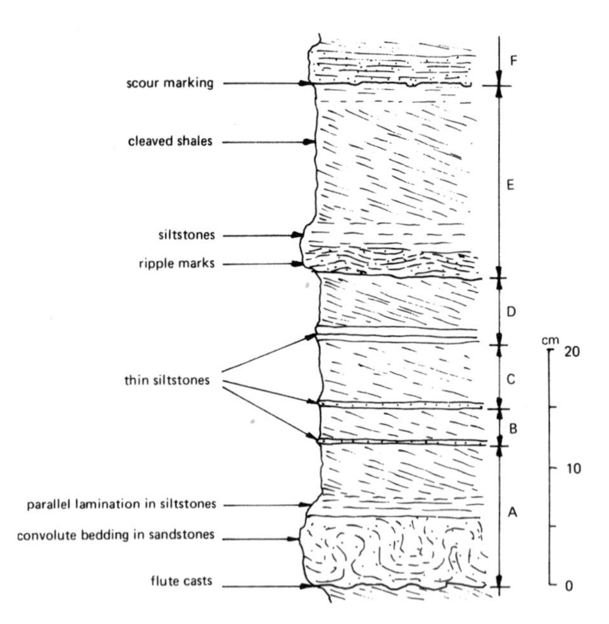

Fig. 25. *Sketch vertical section through part of No. 35. The hammer is resting on the convolute bedded sandstone A. The letters A–F indicate the vertical extent of each turbidite unit.*

thinner units such as C and D, if they are closely examined in the field. The thicker turbidites have slightly irregular bases, caused by erosion of the underlying shales. The shales are slightly cleaved, their laminations dipping at a greater angle than the bedding. Part of this succession is logged in Fig. 25.

No. 36 **Flute casts. Aberystwyth Grits, Lower Silurian.** *Clarach, Aberystwyth, Dyfed (Cardiganshire), Wales.*

The structures shown are infills, by sediment deposited from a turbidity current, of scourings made on the muddy sea floor. A swift current will contain eddies or vortices, like miniature tornadoes, each one suddenly appearing, eroding the sea floor, and quickly losing momentum as it gains sediment. They produce V-shaped impressions, the pointed and deeper end facing upstream, the other end fading out as the mark widens. Within these depressions the coarsest grains carried by the current are subsequently deposited.

Also seen here are a few small tubes of sediment; burrows made by small animals. They wind round and 'over' (in fact beneath) the flute casts, so were made after the deposition of the turbidite.

Nos 37 and 38 **Slumped beds. Upper Ordovician.** *Llangrannog, Dyfed (Cardiganshire), Wales.*

The strata here are composed of thin siltstone and sandstone layers, alternating with shales. Certain horizons, consisting of several beds each, became unstable soon after deposition and slumped, perhaps on a slight slope. The layering was crumpled into a series of extremely irregular folds, with axes at right angles to the direction of slumping, while the coarser, and probably more fluid, sands and silts became concentrated in the troughs of the synclines. With further movement, all the coarser material flowed into these fold troughs to give a slumped layer with rods of sand and silt lying parallel to one another within a chaotically folded mud. Undisturbed layering above and below the slumped beds indicates that slumping occurred before deposition of the overlying strata, and did not affect those beneath. It is thus a feature of the deposition of the beds, and not a later tectonic phenomenon.

No. 39 **Slumping due to loading. Aberystwyth Grits, Lower Silurian.** *Newquay, Dyfed (Cardiganshire), Wales.*

In a turbidite, which is deposited very quickly, internal settling and contortion of the waterladen sediment can easily occur. In the turbidite above the hammer, laminated siltstones (light in colour) overlie the coarser bulk of the unit, whose darker colour indicates a muddy matrix, and which probably contained more water. The denser silts have tended to sink as droplets into the darker sediment, though the process was arrested at an early stage. (In such a two-dimensional section it is not possible to determine whether these structures are in fact droplet-shaped, or are folds.)

No. 40 **Convolute bedding and ripple marks. Aberystwyth Grits, Lower Silurian.** *Aberystwyth, Dyfed (Cardiganshire), Wales.*

Two turbidite flows are seen in section, with contrasting sedimentary characteristics. The lower is strongly convolute bedded, with folds 'leaning' or inclined to the right, the downcurrent direction (compare with No. 42, showing a symmetrical fold formed under purely vertical load). This turbidite grades rapidly above the convoluted layer into a dark shale, which has not been affected by the sedimentary folding, and therefore postdates it. There was probably some erosion of the top of the convoluted layer before deposition of this shale.

The second turbidite rests on the shale with a typically sharp base, in which rounded downward projections may represent infills of organic trails. Bedding in this upper turbidite is undisturbed by any slumping, and two divisions can be seen within it. Up to the level of the pen point, cross lamination inclined to the right can be made out, indicating a current flow in that direction. Above this climbing ripples are present, also in cross section, and with the same current direction. Continuity of the laminations on both the upstream (*stoss*) and downstream (*lee*) slopes shows that there was little erosion on the stoss slopes. The ripples also migrated forwards slightly.

No. 41 **Neptunean dykes. Aberystwyth Grits, Lower Silurian.** *Newquay, Dyfed (Cardiganshire), Wales.*

Two thick turbidite grits are separated by a few centimetres of shales, within which is a sharply defined grit, about 3cm thick, containing conspicuous white grains of feldspar. Three neptunean dykes can be seen injected upwards from this thin grit bed through the overlying shale into the massive grit above. The grit has been forced under pressure, while still waterladen, into the vertical cracks and up into the upper grit, probably driven by the weight of this grit, acting through the intervening mud, which must have been more cohesive than the grit beneath. Well spaced joints within the grits are localized by the dykes. In the shales they are much more closely spaced.

No. 42 **Diapiric structure. Drill core from recent sediments.** *Tremadoc Bay, Gwynedd, Wales.*

The section shown is from a drill core taken through the soft sediment on the floor of Tremadoc Bay, cut lengthwise in half from the originally cylindrical core, encased in a plastic tube. The dark clays are uppermost, and are underlain by a sequence of sands, silts and thin clays. Loading of the denser clays above onto the water-saturated and lighter sequence below has resulted in an upwelling of the lower sediments in a flat-topped dome. The coarsest sands must have been the most fluid: they have lost any internal banding and form a central 'plug' to the structure. The horizontal striations across the section are caused by the saw which was used to cut the core in half.

Such density inversion, or *diapiric* structures, can be found on all scales, from small structures such as that seen here, to major geological structures thousands of metres in diameter. These large diapiric structures occur where salt horizons have been forced up through considerable thicknesses of strata, doming up the surrounding beds to form a *salt dome*. They form an important class of oil reservoirs.

No. 43 **Intraformational clast. Aberystwyth Grits, Lower Silurian.** *Newquay, Dyfed (Cardiganshire), Wales.*

The term *intraformational* is applied to pebbles and other sedimentary inclusions, which were derived from within the rocks in which they are now found. In this case the turbidity current eroded this clast from the sea floor, rolled it up like a swiss roll, and deposited it here. Note that within the 'roll' there is some coarse sediment, exactly like that of the turbidite enclosing it. It appears that the roll was also provided by the current with a filling!

No. 44 **Fossil Patch Reefs in the Wenlock Limestone. Middle Silurian.** *Wenlock Edge, Salop, England.*

The Wenlock Limestone of this quarry consists of an alternating succession of fine beds of nodular bioclastic limestone and of somewhat calcareous shales. In this succession are ellipsoidal masses of unbedded limestone called 'ballstones' by the quarrymen. The ballstones are made up of masses of colonial corals, both rugose and tabulate, and of stromatoporoids. These fossils are in the position of growth with their calices opening upwards. Corals are also to be found in the thin-bedded limestones and shales, but here they are often somewhat wave worn and may be lying in any direction, on their sides and even upside down. The ballstones must have been formed as small coral-stromatoporoid patch reefs on the floor of the shallow current and wave-agitated sea in which the Wenlock Limestone was deposited. They often occur one above the other. The white-coated geologist is examining a large ballstone extending down to the floor of the quarry. Higher up in the face is another and smaller ballstone and another ballstone can be seen just below the soil. Notice how the thin-bedded limestones end abruptly against the lowest and largest ballstone, whilst they are arched up over the smaller middle one. These reef masses must have stood above the level of the surrounding sea floor.

No. 45 **Nodular limestones and shales. Carboniferous.** *Penrhyn, Anglesey, Wales.*

Chemical precipitation is strongly suggested by the nodular and discontinuous limestone bands interbedded with dark shales. It is difficult to determine whether the nodules grew on the sea floor, or were post-depositional. Some are long rod-like bodies, which may have originally been burrows, within which the limestone was later precipitated. The limestones themselves carry a small amount of bitumen formed from organic matter (if struck with a hammer, they produce a slight smell of burning oil). The dark colour of the shales is probably due also to organic matter.

No. 46 **Modern coquina.** *St. Jacut, Brittany, France.*

The shells and shell debris have accumulated on the modern beach under current action, and if entombed beneath more sediment and cemented would form a lens of shelly rock termed a *coquina*. Most of the bivalve shells are disarticulated, that is the valves are separated, and more than 50% are lying convex side uppermost. Many of the shells are broken, and the shell fragments range in size down to sand-sized pieces. The shells themselves come from more than one environment; the cockles are sand burrowers, the mussels surface dwellers attached to rocks, as are the limpets. Thus analysis of such accumulations may not only yield the stratigraphic age of the rock, but also lead to sedimentary and ecological conclusions.

No. 47 **Solution pipes in the Chalk. Upper Cretaceous.** *Castle Limeworks near South Mimms, Hertfordshire, England.*

The discontinuous lines of nodules of black flint show that the Chalk is lying horizontally. A thin, dark-coloured soil with a very irregular base overlies the Chalk and also cuts across the paler sands infilling 'pipes' tapering down into the Chalk. Some of the pipes are continuous, and are vertical. Others (those on the left) are more curved and are therefore cut across obliquely by the working face. The material filling these pipes is identical with the Lower Eocene sands and flint gravel beds which can be seen elsewhere in this quarry resting with a very sharp lithological break, but with no angular discordance, on the Chalk. The pipes in the photograph are only small ones, much larger ones having been exposed in the past as the quarry face was cut backwards. The largest one seen was 6m in diameter at the deepest part of the workings, some 25m below the Eocene/Chalk junction at the top of the quarry.

Piping is frequently seen wherever the Chalk is overlain by sands or gravels. Rain water percolating through the porous beds has caused differential solution of the Chalk, especially along the joints. The overlying deposits collapse as the Chalk is dissolved away. Depressions in the ground may occur over the larger pipes. Near to the Castle Limeworks at Water End, a stream disappears down a group of 'swallow holes' into large pipes.

No. 48 **Corals *in situ* on bedding plane. Carboniferous Limestone.** *Streedagh Point, Co. Sligo, Eire.*

Horizontal limestones form beds about 30cm thick, with partings of shale, and the rock pavement shown is at the top of one of these. Two types of coral can be seen, approximately in growth position. *Lithostrotion*, a colonial coral, forms mound-like masses, while the solitary stick-like corals, thicker than the hammer shaft, are of the genus *Caninia*. These are all lying parallel to the bedding, but may have been upright during growth.

An influx of mud, now forming the shale parting, may have toppled and smothered these corals. Similar corals are present in the succeeding limestone, at the top of the picture, and it is probable that they grew and flourished when the limestone was being deposited.

No. 49 **Ironstone Quarry. Middle Jurassic.** *Warren Farm near Grantham, Lincolnshire, England.*

The sideritic Northampton Ironstone in the left foreground has been heavily oxidized to brown limonite. It is overlain by the pale coloured silts of the Lower Estuarine Series. They contain vertical rootlet markings and were probably laid down in a marsh on the surface of a delta. The overlying well-bedded and well-jointed Lincolnshire Limestone is a normal oolitic limestone deposited in a shallow sea. This method of working, removing the overburden from a considerable width of the ore, is common practice in opencast quarrying.

No. 50 **Stylolitic surface in cross-section. Newmarket Limestone, Lower Ordovician.** *St. Paul's Church, Washington County, Maryland, U.S.A.*

Two prominent stylolitic surfaces can be seen replacing one another below the pencil. The deflection of the beds, as shown in Fig. 26, affords a measure of the thickness of strata dissolved (about 5cm), a calculation

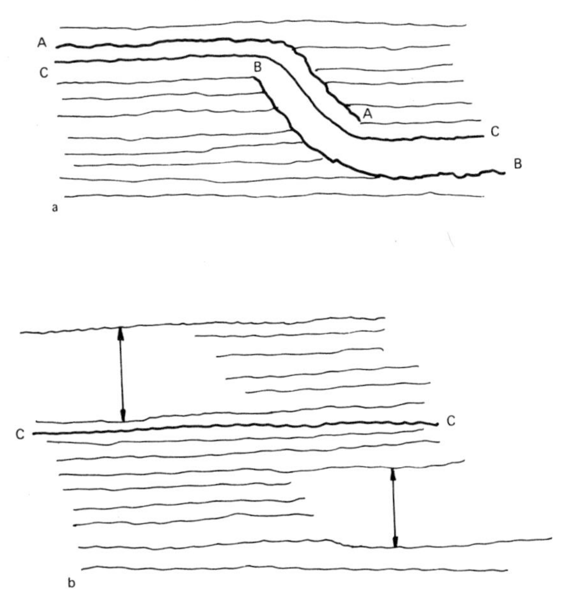

Fig. 26. a *The stylolitic surfaces of No. 50, A–A and B–B.* b *Restoration of the section by straightening surface C–C.*

which is not often possible with stylolites. Within this rock unit, stylolitic surfaces occur at vertical intervals of about 15 cm. If the amount of solution is approximately equal on each surface, then 25% of the rock will have been lost.

No. 51 **Concretionary limestone. Upper Magnesian Limestone, Upper Permian.** *Fulwell, near Sunderland, Durham, England.*

Spherulitic calcitic concretions are set in a matrix of powdery dolomite, so the concretions stand out on a weathered surface. The concretions range in a size from a few millimetres upwards and when large enough form the 'Cannon Ball Limestone'. The larger concretions, below the hammer, are more ellipsoidal in shape and when broken often show concentric banding. These concretions, which may have even more bizarre shapes, have been formed by the segregation of calcite in a deposit that was originally dolomitic.

No. 52 **Conformable strata. Blue Lias, Lower Jurassic.** *Lavernock Point near Penarth, Glamorgan, Wales.*

The cliffs are made up of alternating beds of pale-coloured limestone and darker-hued shale or mudstone. Note how the harder limestone layers project on the broken face of the cliff, that the thicker limestone bands are cut by vertical joints and how the proportion of limestone to shale varies at different levels. The storm beach is made up of limestone fragments, the size of the larger blocks being determined by the spacing of the joints.

No. 53 **The 'Broken Beds'. Purbeck Beds, Upper Jurassic.** *Lulworth Cove, Dorset, England.*

In the top left-hand corner, an alternating succession of thin-bedded limestones and shales dips northwards at about 30°. In the extreme bottom right-hand corner, dark-coloured limestones dip in the same direction. In between are the 'Broken Beds', a jumbled mass of blocks of cream-coloured limestone overlain by marls with darker bands showing over-folding towards the north and then passing upwards into the uniformly dipping succession.

According to one view, the 'Broken Beds' were laid down in tidal (sekbha) flats on the shore of a large shallow gulf similar to parts of the present Persian Gulf. Under such hot climatic conditions, the water covering the flats would often become extremely saline, leading to the precipitation of gypsum and of limestones of chemical origin. The volume change as the gypsum was converted to anhydrite caused brecciation and collapse. The over- and underlying bedded deposits were laid down under less extreme salinity conditions.

Others would regard the brecciation as of tectonic origin. This unit of thin bedded limestones and evaporites, formed under sekbha conditions, acted as an incompetent layer when the area was affected by the Alpine movements. The evaporites flowed plastically, whilst the brittle limestones fractured. The underlying massive limestones and the overlying strata without any interbedded evaporites were tilted but did not break.

No. 54 **Seam of gypsum. Keuper Marl (Upper Triassic).** *Aust Cliff, on the River Severn, Avon, England.*

Interbedded with the reddish marl is one thick and another much thinner seam of gypsum. The thicker seam shows typical fibrous (satin spar) structure and arches up over a nodule of gypsum. Beds of evaporite deposits may reach a thickness of many metres.

No. 55 **Collapse Breccia. Magnesian Limestone, Upper Permian.** *Marsden Cliff, near Sunderland, Durham, England.*

Solution of the underlying evaporites has caused the limestone to collapse and produce spectacular breccias with the blocks of limestone lying at all angles. These collapsed beds are underlain by undisturbed strata and pass upwards into evenly bedded rocks.

No. 56 **Bone Bed. Rhaetic Beds, Triassic/Jurassic.** *Aust near the Severn Toll Bridge, Avon, England.*

Dull black phosphatic nodules and more lustrous teeth, spines and scales of fish are enclosed in a white sandy matrix with small glistening crystals of iron pyrites. A larger, slightly oxidized crystal of pyrites can be seen at the bottom of the specimen. The fish teeth are not noticeably rolled, suggesting that this bone bed is not a condensed deposit due to prolonged winnowing of material, but that a sudden change, probably of salinity, caused mass extinction of the contemporary fish fauna. The abundance of pyrites indicates that the sandy bottom of the body of water in which the bone bed was deposited was an anaerobic (reducing) environment deficient in oxygen, so that the iron sulphates were converted to sulphides.

Nos 57–60 **Coal measures. Lower Carboniferous, opencast coal workings.** *Kilkerran, Ayrshire, Scotland.*

Although these coal measures belong to the Lower, and not the Upper Carboniferous, they are otherwise typical of the Coal Measures of much of northern Europe. They are situated in the small Dailly Coalfield, a downwarped and downfaulted basin. The dark grey shales have been deposited in lagoonal conditions, and tend to pass up into coal seams. The clay becomes darker in colour, with increasing plant debris, both as fragments and as rootlets passing through the rock (No. 60). This reflects silting up of the delta enabling vegetation to grow, and gradually a coal measure forest to become established. The roof of the seam is often a sharp contact, with shales, sometimes marine, or deltaic sandstones. This is the result of drowning of the delta, perhaps with rejuvenation of the rivers feeding and rebuilding the delta. The gradual rebuilding up of the delta eventually leads to the re-establishment of another forest, and repetition of these beds produces a coal measure cyclothem of the type illustrated in Fig. 12. Limestone is not present in the beds exposed here, but is sometimes found as part of the marine sequence.

Both the general lithology and structural state of these rocks is shown in No. 58. To the left are coals, shales, ironstone and seat earths (seen in close-up in No. 60) overlain by massive sandstones and grits. A near-vertical fault complex separates these sandstones from more coal-bearing beds, in which is a coal seam cut by a thrust (No. 57). In No. 59 light coloured and rusty weathering sandstones and grits of Millstone Grit type succeed the coal. The grains are almost all of quartz, up to a few millimetres in diameter, cemented by a siderite matrix. The section shown in No. 59 also contains a nodular layer of ironstone, just above the hammer. This type of deposit was sometimes mined with the coal, as a source of iron ore, and often contains sufficient carbonaceous material to enable it to be smelted without the addition of much coal.

No. 61 **Concretion. Whitehouse Beds, Upper Ordovician.** *Girvan, Scotland.*

An oval-shaped concretion (probably circular when viewed from above) is lying within vertically inclined siltstones and mudstones. The siltstone laminae pass through the concretion without interruption, hence it was formed after deposition, without disturbance of the bedding. The laminae are however bent round the concretion, so that the succession as measured on either side of it is about two-thirds of that measured through it. Two explanations may be offered. Firstly the concretion grew and hardened, by precipitation of a carbonate matrix, before compaction of the surrounding sediment. Alternatively, the chemical precipitation caused actual physical expansion of the concretion. Detailed study of the concretion and the surrounding rock would be necessary to resolve this.

No. 62 **Cone-in-cone concretion. Aberystwyth Grits, Lower Silurian.** *Aberystwyth, Dyfed (Cardiganshire), Wales.*

Concretions containing cone-in-cone structure are common features of the shales and mudstones of a turbidite sequence, often lying within particular bedding planes as flattish discs. Here one is seen in partial cross-section; it is discus shaped, with quite sharp edges where the concretion tapers into the bedding. The bases of the cones appear as small circular discs on the upper surface.

No. 63 **Flint in Chalk. Upper Cretaceous.** *Ballymagarry Quarry, Portrush, N. Ireland.*

The cherts, or flints, of the Chalk vary from tabular to nodular in habit. Occasionally they form thin sheets, but more commonly occur as horizons of discontinuous nodules, each of which forms an irregular mass, with protuberances both upwards and downwards. Their colour varies from dark brown to pale grey, with a white rim. Cavities may be present within the flint, infilled with unconsolidated sediment and small fossils (*chalk meal*), while calcareous fossils, such as sea urchins or brachiopods may be embedded in or completely surrounded by the flint without alteration of their shells to silica. Many chalk sea urchins preserved in flint are, in fact, represented by the flint infilling of the test.

No. 64 **Chert bodies in dolomite. Durness Limestone, Cambro-Ordovician.** *Durness, Sutherland, Scotland.*

The group known as the Durness

Limestone contains within it extensive dolomites, often with conspicuous chert bodies. These have grown by replacement of the dolomite, since the bedding planes are continuous from the dolomite across their boundaries.

Within the cherts, the laminations of the dolomite are much more conspicuous. Above the penknife, downwarping of the bedding is visible both within the chert body and to one side of it. This may have been due to solution of soft strata, and subsequent flexure of the layers above, to produce a pseudo-unconformity. Actual breakup of laminae can be seen below the knife, where jumbled flakes form what has been described as a *flake conglomerate*. Additionally, some volume change may have accompanied the growth of the cherts, further disrupting the bedding, and finally compaction took place within the unaltered rock, after chert growth.

No. 65 **Septarian nodule in shales. Upper Ordovician.** *Penwhapple Glen, Girvan, Ayrshire, Scotland.*

The periphery of the nodule is formed of brown-stained carbonate which has resisted weathering better than the interior. The latter is of coarse crystals, showing a faint colour banding which is the result of their deposition inwards from the cracks. Note that if the cracks were to be closed up again, the nodule would be much smaller, yet the periphery is uncracked, and therefore would not shrink without becoming crumpled. It appears that the inside must have been cracking and pieces moving apart, at the same time as the periphery was growing.

No. 66 **Irregular burrow system. Lower Carboniferous shales.** *Hook Head, Co. Wexford, Eire.*

Light coloured siltstones are succeeded by dark shales, the bedding planes dipping gently to the left. An irregular system of burrows in the lower siltstone is infilled with the dark shale from above. It is not possible to determine whether the shale infilling was emplaced in the burrows after the death of the burrowing animals, or whether already deposited dark shale was dragged down into the burrows by the animals.

No. 67 **Burrow mining system. Aberystwyth Grits, Lower Silurian.** *Aberystwyth, Dyfed (Cardiganshire), Wales.*

Burrow systems are often concentrated at interfaces between different sediments, in this case the base of a turbidite, resting on fine shales. This surface, perhaps the sea floor before deposition of the turbidite, was rich in organic content. The burrow system radiates from a central point, which marks the site of a vertical burrow, passing up from the observer into the turbidite, communicating with the sea floor for a clean water supply.

No. 68 **Sand-infilled burrows. Lower Cambrian.** *Ullapool, N.W. Highlands, Scotland.*

Irregular, but predominantly vertical, burrow systems can be seen in the 30cm of strata above the penknife. The more massive beds above and below are quartz-rich sandstones, in which the burrows, themselves infilled with the same sediment, are not conspicuous, but are present. The middle bed contains an admixture of finer sediment, in which the burrows stand out, infilled with a purer quartz sand. At the bottom and top of this bed the sediment is more muddy and the burrows more prominent. They are also inclined to the left. This may be an original feature: the burrows were inclined in response to a water current. Conversly their aspect may have been caused by deformation: the more muddy layers are less resistant and would yield to shearing along the bedding planes as one bed slipped over the next, dragging the tubes with it.

No. 69 **Trace fossils. Lower Lias, Lower Jurassic.** *Lyme Regis, Dorset, England.*

This bedding plane of a block of typical blue-grey Blue Lias limestone, lying loose on the beach, shows the burrows and trails made by a variety of organisms. To the right of the scale some trails can be seen to cut through those that had already been made. The thin white lines crossing the block are calcite veins.

No. 70 **Doubtful trace fossils. Grès Armoricain, Ordovician.** *Camaret, Presqu'île de Crozon, Brittany, France.*

Varied marks of this general type are commonly found on bedding planes, and it is often difficult to decide whether they are due to movement by currents of non-organic particles, or of dead shells or organisms, or are made by the life activities of an organism.

The upper surface of a micaceous sandstone unit faces the camera; it bears three horse-shoe shaped depressions which are similarly aligned. These are very similar to those made by the modern king-crab, as it faces upstream and slightly digs in with its front, elevating the rear and gills. Although no fossil king-crabs have been found in these rocks, the markings suggest that similar animals, or perhaps trilobites, made them.

No. 71 ***Palaeodictyon* and other trace fossils. Aberystwyth Grits, Lower Silurian.** *Aberystwyth, Dyfed (Cardiganshire), Wales.*

Two main types of trace fossil are present: thicker winding traces and thinner but more widespread traces forming a distinctive grid pattern, with a mesh size of about 2cm. The latter, given the generic name *Palaeodictyon*, is interpreted as a system of 'mining' burrows along the sediment interface, now infilled with the overlying grit. Erosion of the shale from the surface has resulted in the tubes appearing in relief on the undersurface of the turbidite. Other markings on the surface are inorganic; fine cracks running from top to bottom are joints, others which appear as very fine white lines are thin veins infilled with quartz.

No. 72 **Faulted syncline and anticline. Ordovician conglomerates and shales.** *Cemaes Bay, Anglesey, Wales.*

The massive grits and conglomerates occupying most of the cliff rest on Pre-Cambrian schists and quartzites of the Mona Complex (the outcrop of the unconformity illustrated in No. 7 is just to the right of this picture). They are succeeded by cherty shales, seen in the down-faulted core of the syncline and also present just out of the picture to the left, on the flank of the anticline.

Faults A, B and C (Fig. 27) are steep reverse faults, downthrowing to the right, and associated with numerous quartz veins. Fault D is approximately vertical, with a downthrow to the left, and could be regarded either as a normal or a reverse fault.

No. 73 **Slaty cleavage. Lower Silurian.** *Rhayader, Powys (Radnorshire), Wales.*

The slaty cleavage in this exposure is sufficiently well developed to form the main planar structure, along which the rock will preferentially split. The bedding planes are however clearly shown by slight changes in lithology, particularly by the dark blue-grey band, about 8cm thick, in the centre of the photograph. Below this is a thinner current-bedded sandstone in which the cleavage planes are not well developed. The intersection of the bedding and cleavage planes, which forms a linear structure parallel to the local fold axes, is well seen on the cleavage planes. The beds are not inverted.

No. 74 **Post folding cleavage. Ordovician turbidites.** *Portandea, Ayrshire, Scotland.*

The camera is looking along the *axial trace* (the outcrop of the axial plane) of a syncline, steeply plunging away from the observer (Fig. 28). Each turbidite shows good grading, from a sharp upper contact with shale, to a lower passage into shale. Therefore, the succession is inverted, the beds becoming younger down the succession, and the syncline or synform is said to be *downward facing*.

A cleavage, parallel to the hammer handle, is also present in the shales, though it does not penetrate the coarser portions of the turbidites. Since it is not folded with the syncline, and is not parallel to its axial

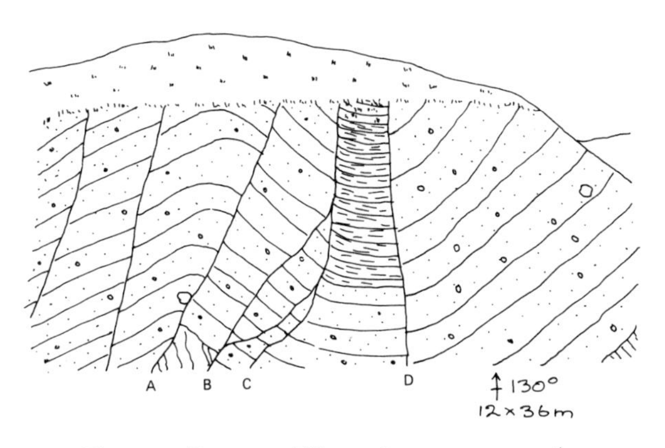

Fig. 27. *Exposure of No. 72 drawn as a cross section.*

plane, it is interpreted as being formed after the fold.

No. 75 **Vertical strata. Skomer Group, Lower Silurian.** *Marloes Bay, Dyfed (Pembrokeshire), Wales.*

The beds exposed here are shallow water siltstones with more resistant orange weathering sandstones. The vertical strata are cut by the Pleistocene–modern wavecut platform at beach level, and also by the older and higher Tertiary platform at the cliff top.

No. 76 **Faulted anticline and syncline. Aberystwyth Grits, Lower Silurian.** *Clarach, Dyfed (Cardiganshire), Wales.*

The outcrops, on a wavecut platform, give an appearance, on a small scale, of a geological relief map. In the foreground an anticline plunges gently to the south (left); beyond it is a syncline with an almost horizontal axis, and a second anticline is less obviously seen further across. The directions of strike are given by the outcrops of the grits, accentuated by the rock pools; note how the strikes of the limbs of the nearer anticline converge in the direction of plunge.

The gully in the background marks the site of an important fault; beyond it the structures do not match with the folds just described. There is a complex anticlinal hinge, whose minor folds can be seen in cross-section, on the side of the fault gully (Fig. 29).

No. 77 **Conjugate folds. Old Head Series, Silurian.** *Near Louisburgh, Co. Mayo, Eire.*

Two complementary folds form a *conjugate* set, caused by compression

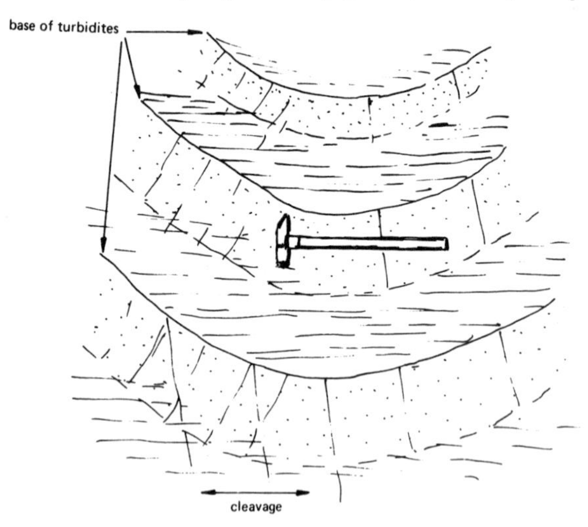

Fig. 28. *The inverted fold of No. 74.*

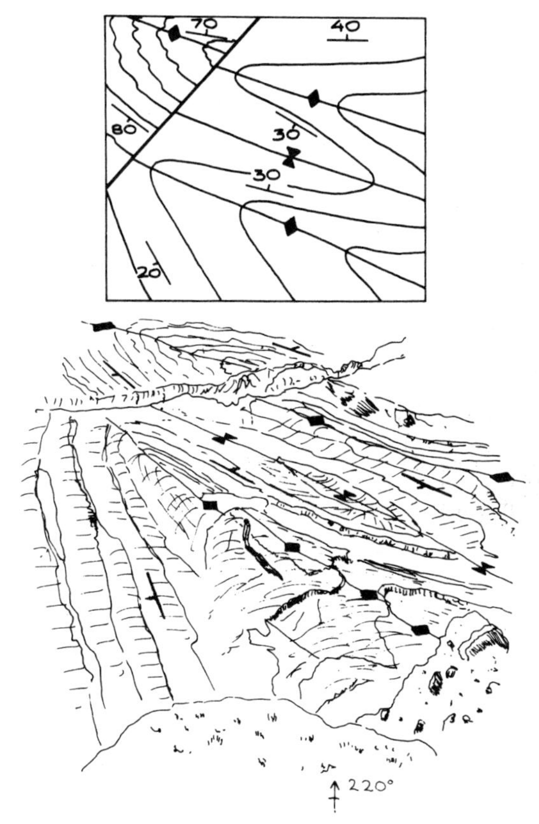

Fig. 29. *Sketch of No. 76, with diagrammatic map above.*

parallel to the bedding planes. Each fold is in reality a fold pair, an anticline and a syncline, close together. Each fold pair defines an incipient fault, with sense of movement indicated in Fig. 30. Quartz veining is associated with the structure.

The Old Head Series is a formation of sandstones, siltstones, and shales, of 'Old Red Sandstone' facies, deposited in a non-marine environment.

No. 78 **Bedding/cleavage relationship in folded rocks. Aberystwyth Grits, Lower Silurian.** *Clarach, Dyfed (Cardiganshire), Wales.*

The exposure is on the flank of an anticline, whose axial plane lies to

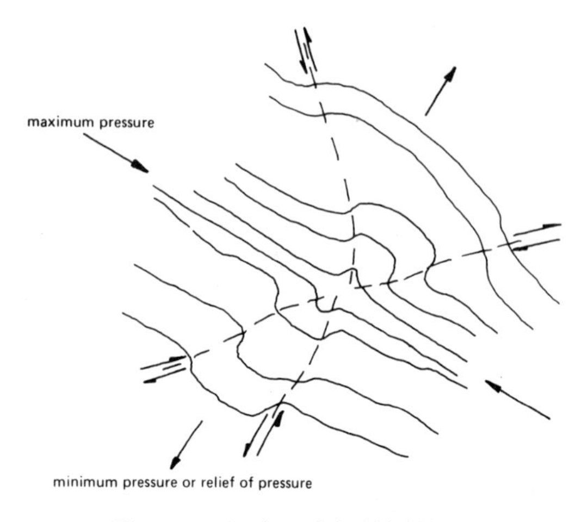

Fig. 30. *Analysis of the folds of No. 77.*

the left of the picture, and demonstrates the use of slaty cleavage to determine the major structure (p. 41, Figs 7, 31). The slaty cleavage has a higher dip than the bedding, given by the turbidite bed. The vertical face of the exposure is determined by a joint plane, developed in both the turbidite and the shales. On the turbidite can be seen the faint markings of feather fracture (Fig. 31a).

No. 79 **Overturned beds on fold limb. Castell Limestone and shales, Ordovician.** *Abereiddy Bay, Dyfed (Pembrokeshire), Wales.*

Like No. 78, this is the vertical face of an exposure determined by a joint plane, with both bedding and cleavage planes end on to the observer. Bedding planes are clearly seen in the platy limestone, and bedding can also be seen in the junction between it and the shales to the right. Within the latter a slaty cleavage is the dominant structure, also dipping to the left, but less steeply than the bedding. The major structure to the right (south) is a syncline, whose axis runs through the nearby Abereiddy Bay (Fig. 31b).

No. 80 **Tectonic alignment of pebbles. Rhinog Grits, Lower Cambrian.** *Barmouth, Gwynedd (Merionethshire), Wales.*

The fine conglomerate contains white and blue-white quartz pebbles, rounded or angular in outline, and creamy shale flakes. The latter especially are aligned parallel to one another to define the cleavage planes (perpendicular to the plane of the paper and parallel to the pencil). The bedding of the rock is also perpendicular to the paper, but parallel to the edge of the rock in the bottom right hand corner. The rusty colour here is due to the weathering of iron pyrite crystals to iron oxide.

In the process of rotation into the cleavage planes, the quartz pebbles have not been distorted or recrystallized, but simply mechanically reorientated. The shale flakes may have additionally been flattened.

No. 81 **Fracture cleavage. Old Red Sandstones (Devonian).** *St. Ann's Head, Dyfed (Pembrokeshire), Wales.*

The strata seen are approximately horizontal sandstones and silty mudstones. The lower beds are slightly coarser, with abundant crossbedding. Towards the top of the photograph are scattered calcareous concretions, cream-coloured on fresh surfaces, but weathering back to form irregular hollows. These are typical flood plain sediments, forming repeated cycles and each laid down by a single flood, followed by drying out of the plain. Similar deposits are being formed today, and in hot dry climates with seasonal

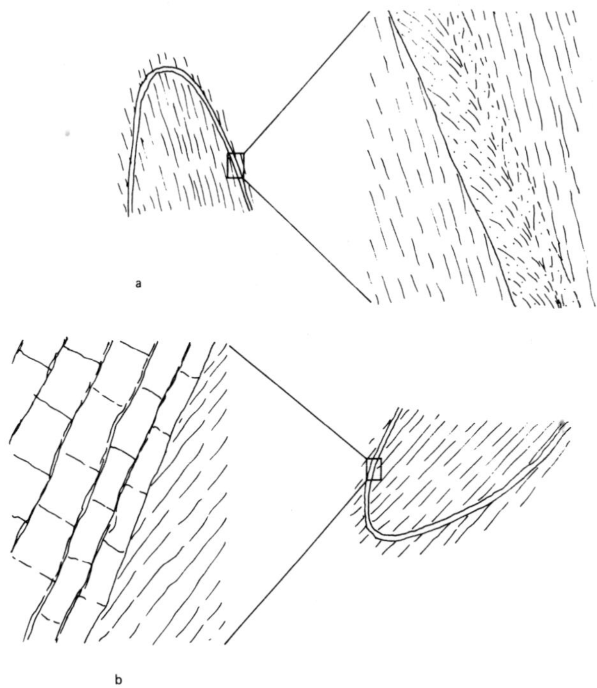

Fig. 31. *Sketches of Nos 78 and 79, indicating their position with relation to the major structures.*

rainfall evaporation of the groundwater between the floods leads to precipitation of the calcareous concretions. They may be sufficiently concentrated at certain horizons to form a concretionary limestone, a *caliche*.

The fracture cleavage is developed as vertical planes 2–5 cm apart. There is little sign of deformation of the rock between them, but they form the principal planes of weakness along which the rock is weathering.

No. 82 **Minor folding on a major fold limb. Lower Carboniferous sandstones and shales.** *Old Head of Kinsale, Co. Cork, Eire.*

These folds illustrate well the minor structures used to elucidate the major fold pattern. The more resistant grits maintain a fairly constant thickness in the folds (though some thickening is seen in the hinges) while the shales between them vary markedly in thickness, especially in the hinges. A neptunean dyke is present at the core of the central syncline (Fig. 32), and may have been injected during the folding and development of the cleavage.

The sea cave and wavecut platform are related to sea level at or near that of the present day. At the cliff top is a good soil section, with soil creep just visible in the right background.

No. 83 **Isoclinal fold and thrust. Devonian limestones and shales.** *Elberry Cove, Paignton, Devonshire, England.*

Tightly folded strata are here overthrust along a near horizontal thrust plane, with fault drag showing that the upper strata have been displaced to the left.

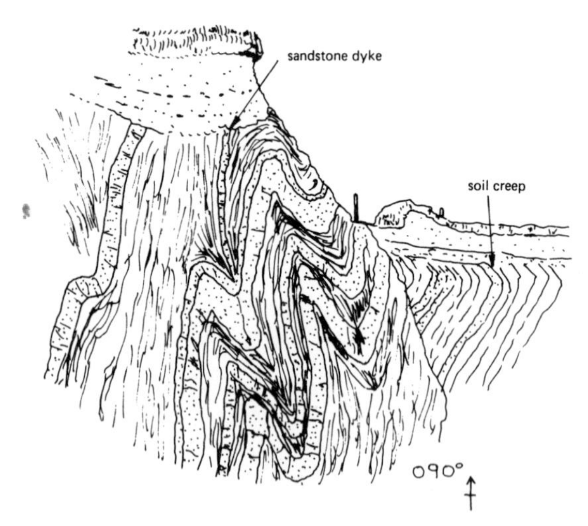

Fig. 32. *Sketch of part of No. 82.*

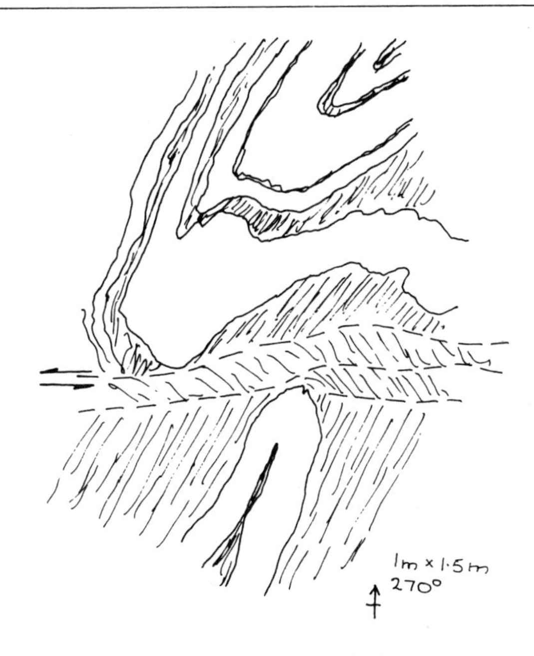

Fig. 33. *Isocline and thrust of No. 83.*

Above the thrust folding is inclined, with overturned limbs and apparent thickening in the hinges. Some horizons have also been sheared out. Below the thrust folding is even tighter. A perfectly isoclinal anticline (Fig. 33) is present immediately to the left of the hammer.

No. 84 **Growth fibres and slickensides on a fault plane. Aberystwyth Grits, Lower Silurian.** *Aberystwyth, Dyfed (Cardiganshire), Wales.*

Growth fibres of brown-stained calcite are particularly evident in the lower half of this photograph, as several overlapping sheets, each composed of a number of parallel fibres. In contrast, against the scale are grooves (slickensides) cut in the rock surface by movement of the rock on the near side of the fault plane, now eroded away.

It is probable that these grooves are of comparatively recent date, and were caused by slippage of the now vanished rock face, during weathering and while it slipped down slope before falling away completely to the foot of the cliff. Such grooves can often be found on fallen blocks, and sometimes small pieces of rock fall into the slightly open crack of the fault plane, causing gouging of the two walls during the slippage.

No. 85 **Whin Sill and Lower Carboniferous sediments.** *Cullernose Point, near Howick, Northumberland, England.*

In the foreground are gently folded Lower Carboniferous limestones. Behind these beach exposures, the cliffs to the right show the Whin Sill, a quartz–dolerite sill which can be traced across much of north-east England with a maximum thickness of 80m. The dark coloured rocks of the sill show very well developed columnar jointing at right angles to the top and bottom of the sill. The left hand cliffs expose a succession of massive sandstones, upfaulted against the sill.

No. 86 **Normal fault in shales. Kimmeridge shales, Jurassic.** *Kimmeridge Bay, Dorset, England.*

The normal fault shown downthrows to the right, by more than 5m (the prominent bed above the figure cannot be matched on the upthrow side). The shales are considerably shattered on the downthrow side, there is appreciable bending of the strata adjacent to the fault (*fault drag*), while the thicker bed has been closely jointed.

No. 87 **Low angle fault in Chalk. Upper Cretaceous.** *Flamborough Head, Humberside, England.*

This is an unusual normal fault, in that its dip is very low. It is a clean cut fracture with only slight drag on either side of the fault plane, along which there is a thin belt of crushed rock.

No. 88 **Normal fault.** *Broadsands Bay, Paignton, Devonshire, England.*

This normal fault, throwing Triassic sandstones against harder Devonian limestones, has a throw of the order of tens of metres, and a shatter zone about 20m wide (Fig. 34). The sandstones dip away from the fault plane,

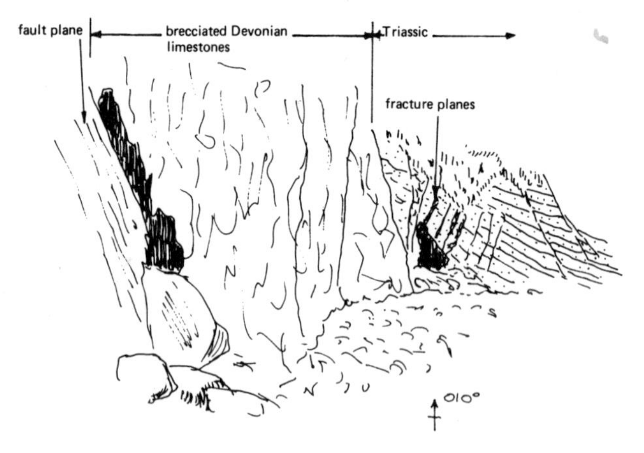

Fig. 34. *Normal fault (No. 88).*

due not to drag on the fault plane but to a regional dip. The shatter zone is composed of two belts, one in each rock type. In the sandstones, a series of planes is developed with an opposing dip to the main fault plane. Each is infilled with breccia and calcite crystals with a complex growth history (No. 89). The limestones are also brecciated and recemented with crystalline calcite, but in this belt there is no colour difference between the components. In the foreground, a sharply cut fault plane is one of a number of planes, within the shatter zone, along which the total movement within the fault was accomplished. The blocks of limestone in the left foreground have fallen from undeformed Devonian limestones, beyond the shatter zone. Coastal erosion has worked back to the fault zone, removing the softer Triassic sandstones and cutting a sea cave in the background.

Many important faults, however, with wide zones of shattering and brecciation, are not well exposed, as the broken rock is easily weathered and eroded. Consequently, a depression is formed, with little exposure within it. The Great Glen Fault, in Scotland, is a large scale example of such a depression, in this case deepened additionally by glacial erosion.

No. 89 **Calcite and sediment infilling a vug. Triassic Sandstones.** *Broadsands, Paignton, Devonshire, England.*

A complex history of deposition and erosion of calcite can be seen in this vug infilling. The vug is on the downthrow side of a normal fault, downfaulting red Triassic sandstones against Devonian shales and limestones (No. 88). A wide shatter zone is developed in the sandstones, including cavities, which are now infilled with calcite and sediment. The process was episodic, with some

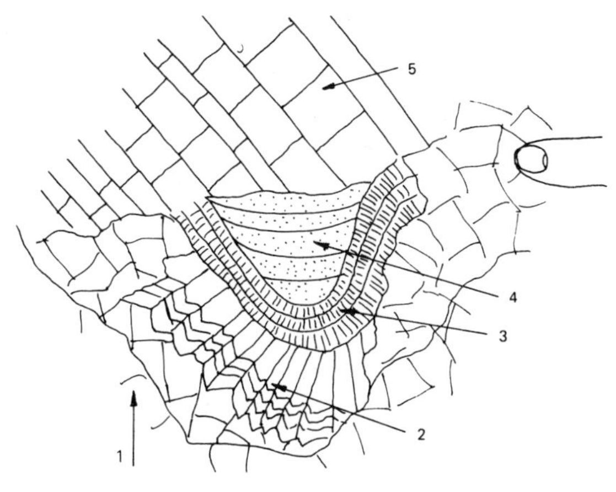

Fig. 35. *Sketch of vug in No. 89, showing the order of deposition of the calcite crystals.*

erosion or solution of calcite alternating with its deposition. Five types of infill can be recognized in the exposure (Fig. 35):

1. Irregular intergrowth of crystals.

2. Growth of large crystals from a face into a void, with successive stages of growth marked by bands of impurities.

3. Small scale alternation of calcite crystals with impurities.

4. Deposition of sediment in a depression. The surface of the layers (the bedding planes) are a fossil 'spirit level' indicating the attitude of the strata during their deposition.

5. Deposition of calcite above the sediment, as a single crystal.

Deposition was not necessarily in the order given, though layers 2, 3 and 4 were deposited successively.

No. 90 **Small normal fault in limestones.** *Old Quarry, Triangle Point, Torquay, Devonshire, England.*

Massive Devonian limestones dip gently away from the camera. The development of a normal fault can be seen from top to bottom of the photograph. Above the hammer is a zone of warping, crossed by tension gashes. Below the hammer there is a dislocation, with warping, or *fault drag*, still evident, and tension gashes are also present. Note that the relationship of the tension gashes to the fault indicates the direction of movement (Fig. 36), as well as the warping of the strata; they make an 'arrow' with the fault plane pointing in the direction of relative movement of the wall of the fault on which they occur.

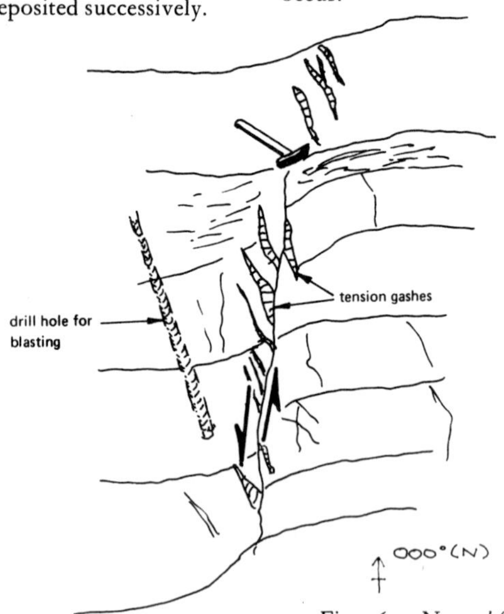

Fig. 36. *Normal fault (No. 90).*

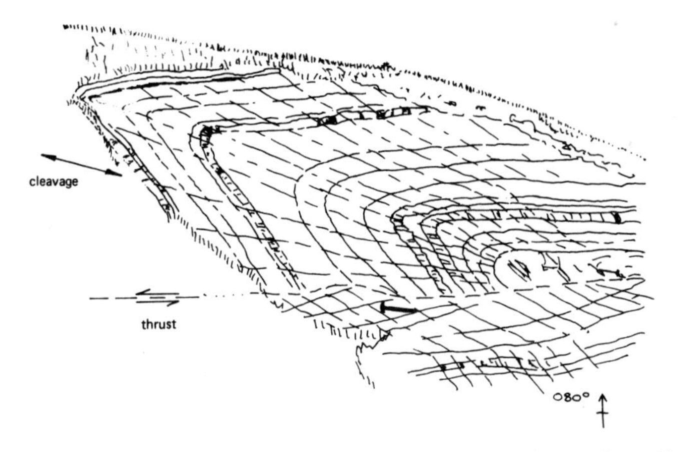

Fig. 37. *The inclined fold and thrust of No. 91. A hammer outline has been added to give scale.*

No. 91 **Inclined fold and thrust in limestones. Middle Devonian.** *Hope's Nose, Torquay, Devonshire, England.*

A horizontal thrust here separates a near horizontal succession of limestones from a strongly inclined and overturned anticline. This fold is variable in its geometry; in the uppermost beds (to the left) it appears as a straight-limbed or chevron fold, with considerable thickening in the hinge zone, whereas further to the right the hinge zone is more rounded, with less thickening (Fig. 37). This is probably related to lithological differences, the upper beds being more shaly and able to flow, the lower more massive and resistent. A crude cleavage is also seen, forming a good cleavage fan, radiating from the core of the fold. The thrust has probably replaced a complementary syncline.

Nos 92 and 93 **Folding passing into thrusting. Coal Measures, Upper Carboniferous.** *Saundersfoot, Dyfed (Pembrokeshire), Wales.*

Inclined folds may pass into thrust faults; two stages of this process are illustrated here. In No. 92 (Fig. 38a) an anticline and a syncline represent the earlier stage; some small thrusts are present along the synclinal hinge. In this exposure the rocks are fine sandstones alternating with shales. The second stage is shown in No. 93 (Fig. 38b), in which the thrust has replaced the common limb between the two folds, and the axial zone of the anticline. The massive sandstones within the syncline are repeated on the left, above the head of the figure, and vertical separation of about 3m can be measured perpendicular to the fault. Movement along the fault plane was more than this, but it is not possible to measure it.

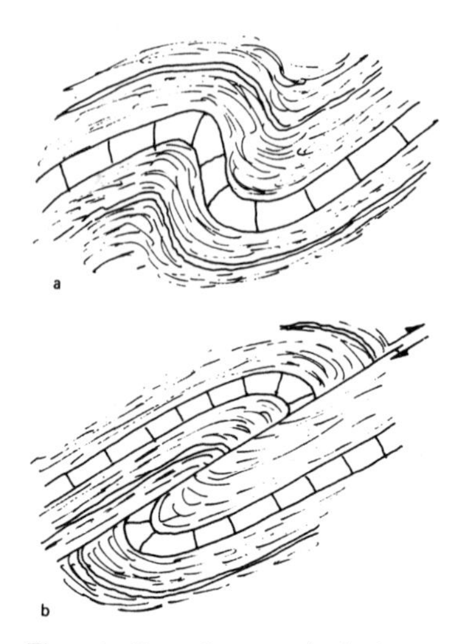

Fig. 38. *Successive stages in the formation of a thrust.* a *No. 92.* b *No. 93.*

No. 94 **The Carmel Head Thrust.** *Carmel Head, Anglesey, Wales.*

This is the type locality for the Carmel Head Thrust, one of the best known thrust planes in southern Britain. Along its mapped outcrop it thrusts a variety of rock types within the Pre-Cambrian Mona Complex over Ordovician and Silurian rocks to the south, here green schists over cleaved shales. The thrust plane is seen in section by the rucksack, while to the left the schists have been removed by erosion to reveal the surface beneath the plane – the *sole* of the thrust. There is little alteration in either rock group along the thrust, only a crush zone some 10–20cm thick which is weathered back into the low cliff.

No. 95 **Low-dipping thrust. Tormitchell Limestone, Upper Ordovician.** *Tormitchell Quarry, Ayrshire, Scotland.*

The Tormitchell Limestone here consists of 10–20cm beds of limestone, separated by muddy partings. It is folded tightly on axes running towards the observer. The thrust plane is marked by a 20-cm thick vein of calcite, with the major break just below it. The overthrust mass has moved to the right, while the thrust post-dates the folds, cutting cleanly across them.

No. 96 **Conjugate fault sets. Lower Ordovician tuffs and shales.** *Abereiddy Bay, Dyfed (Pembrokeshire), Wales.*

Conjugate sets of faults are well developed in the more competent tuffs; the two most prominent faults cancelling each other out where they meet in the shales beneath (though this succession is in fact overturned, the shales being younger than the tuffs). Small sets of tension gashes mark the sites of incipient faults. The low dipping faults are almost horizontal thrusts, while the complementary faults are high-angle reverse faults (Fig. 39).

No. 97 **Tear faults. Whitehouse Beds, Upper Ordovician.** *Girvan, Ayrshire, Scotland.*

Light grey shales alternate with thin sandstones, and dip vertically. Two tear faults are marked by thin quartz veins. Complementary sinistral and dextral faults indicate that the rocks have been shortened perpendicular to the bedding, with relief of pressure along the strike of the bedding (Fig. 40).

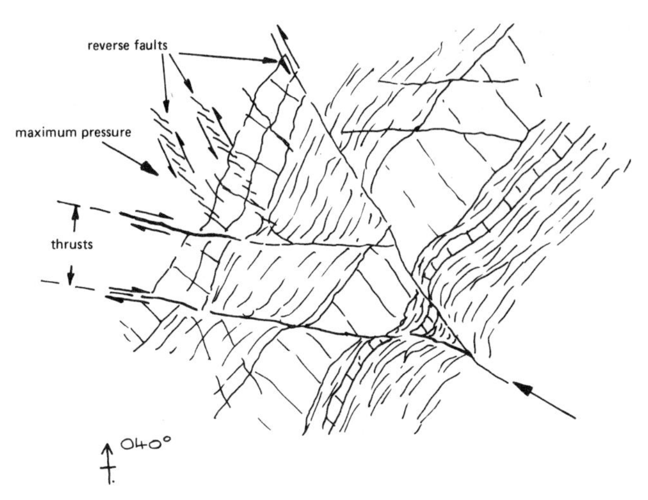

Fig. 39. *Analysis of the conjugate faults of No. 96.*

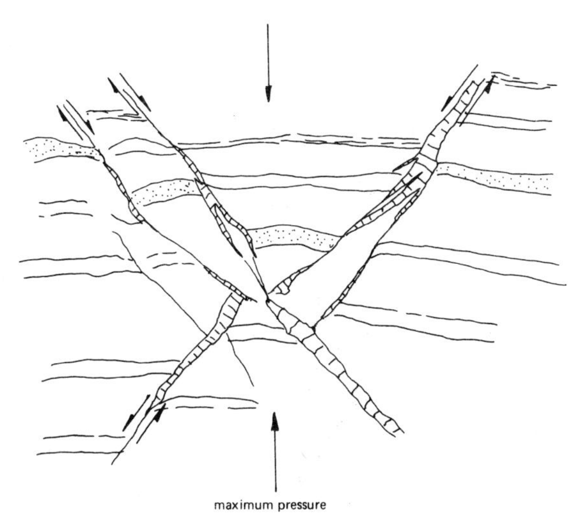

Fig. 40. *Analysis of the conjugate tear faults of No. 97.*

No. 98 **Fibrous quartz vein infilling a fault. Ffestiniog Flags, Upper Cambrian.** *Borth-y-gest, Gwynedd (Merionethshire), Wales.*

The quartz vein is formed of a series of fibres of quartz which have grown as the walls of the vein have moved apart, with a direction of movement shown by the arrows in Fig. 41. Small tension veins are also present, on the left of the large vein; they show a sense of movement which agrees with that of the quartz fibres (cf. No. 90).

No. 99 **Mineralized quartz vein. Lower Silurian.** *Cwm Ystwyth, Dyfed (Cardiganshire), Wales.*

The surface shows the minerals infilling one side of a vein in sandstones, the other side having been eroded or mined away. The grey areas to the right are brecciated fragments from the wall of the vein. In this area are resinous blue-black crystals of the zinc sulphide, *sphalerite* or *blende*, which has crystallized directly on the wall rock in the top right hand corner. Surrounding the blocks and covering the rest of the wall are quartz crystals, which covered the blende and the brecciated blocks, and represent a second stage of crystallization in the vein. Most have terminal prisms facing the camera, indicating that they grew into a void, a liquid-filled cavity.

No. 100 **Tension gashes. Upper Carboniferous.** *Millook Haven, Cornwall, England.*

A spectacular quartz infilled vein system is exposed on a bedding plane of a graded sandstone sequence. A sequence of sets of veins can be made

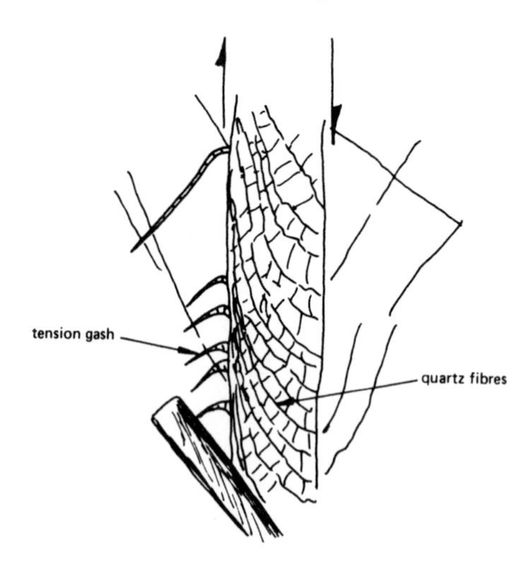

Fig. 41. *Quartz vein of No. 98.*

out, as indicated in Fig. 42 (which is not an accurate drawing of the system). The main veins (B) cut through earlier veins (A), which have been bent round during the movement responsible for producing the B veins. A thin brown vein (C) is later than the B veins, while a fault (D), of unknown sense of movement, appears to be the last event.

No. 101 **Pyritized and silicified shales. Lower Silurian.** *Parys Mountain, Anglesey, Wales.*

Complex relationships can often be seen in ore bodies which are large enough to have been worked commercially. The rock here, before mineralization, was a very well cleaved slate, of almost commercial quality. It has since been silicified in irregular masses, the chlorite and clay minerals of the slate being replaced by a granular mass of quartz crystals. The resulting rock is flinty, with all traces of cleavage healed up. It is also traversed by irregular veins of copper and iron pyrites, one passing through the centre of the picture. On either side, iron pyrites crystals are present in the silicified shale, becoming more sparse away from the vein. A later white quartz vein, without any pyrite, contrasts with the earlier mineralization. The weathered rock surfaces have a brown colour, as the iron pyrites is leached to iron oxide (limonite) and free sulphur.

No. 102 **Ptygmatic Folds in quartz veins. Silurian phyllites.** *Croagh Patrick, Co. Mayo, Eire.*

Low grade phyllites, with the foliation planes exactly parallel to the bedding, dip to the left. In this

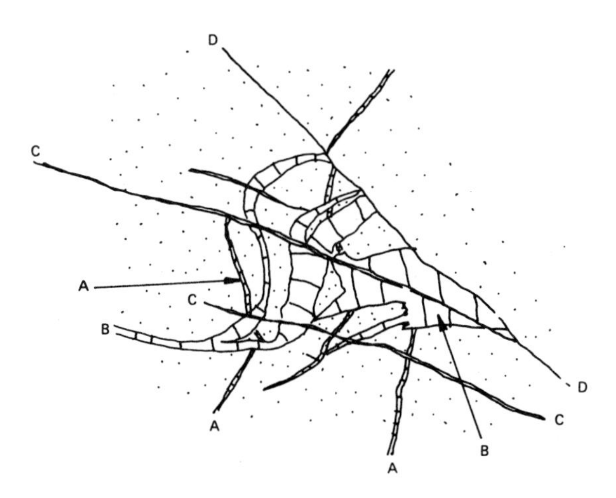

Fig. 42. *Semi-diagrammatic sketch to illustrate the sequence of vein emplacement in No. 100.*

well-laminated rock a quartz vein is emplaced, with intricate, though even, folding. This folding may have been 'built in' during the emplacement of the vein, or may reflect a later folding of an originally straight vein. The former explanation is suggested by the course of the vein just left of the hammer handle, where it splits into two, the two parts having opposing folds (Fig. 43).

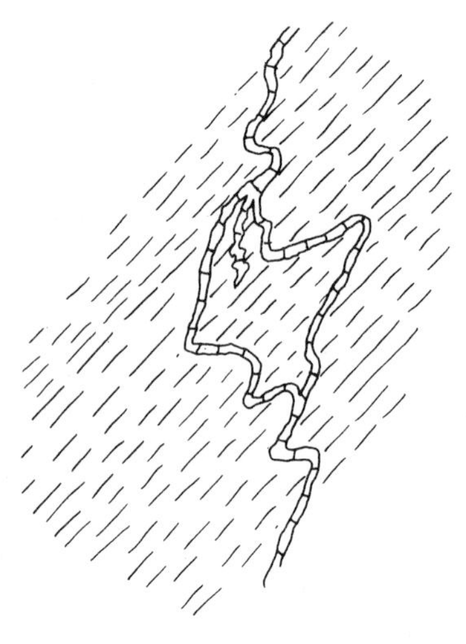

Fig. 43. *Enlargement of part of the ptygmatic quartz vein in No. 102.*

No. 103 **Joints in cementstones. Upper Jurassic.** *Kimmeridge Bay, Dorset, England.*

Cementstones are fine-grained and finely-laminated argillaceous limestones, here interbedded with shales. They resist erosion more easily than the softer shales, and form ledges gently dipping across the shore. An extremely regular joint system is present, two sets of vertical joints crossing one another at right angles, and it should be noted that, unlike faults, one set of joints is not cut by the other. Development of both sets may have been simultaneous.

No. 104 **Scarp in basalts and volcanic neck.** *Co. Antrim coast, N. Ireland.*

Red sandstones and conglomerates of both the Devonian and Trias continental sequences form the lower ground in the right hand middle distance. They are followed by later Mesozoic rocks in the long ridge of Lurigethan, which is capped by near horizontal basalt lavas of the Tertiary Igneous Province. Individual flows form separate bands along the ridge (Fig. 44).

The volcanic neck of Tievebulliagh forms a dark prominence in the right background, at this level of erosion punched through the Lower Basalts. The pipe contains masses of the Interbasaltic Bed (p. 190) which must have fallen down some 150m from the presumed position of the Bed, now well above the present-day erosion level. This was the site of a palaeolithic axe factory, based on the hornfels recrystallized from the Interbasaltic masses. Its products have been identified at a number of sites throughout the British Isles – an early example of an international export trade!

No. 105 **Joint plane with feather fracture. Drosgol Grits, Upper Ordovician.** *Carn Owen, Dyfed (Cardiganshire), Wales.*

A 1-metre thick bed of coarse sandstone dips to the left, with a joint plane perpendicular to the bedding facing the camera. The feather fracture shown is a result of the propagation of the joint, in two directions from the zone indicated (Fig. 45). Similar patterns, called *percussion fractures*, can often be seen on the surfaces of rock broken with a hammer.

Nos 106 and 107 **Non-welded and welded tuffs. Ordovician.** *Yr Arddu, Snowdonia, Gwynedd, Wales.*

The material in the non-welded tuff consists of angular blocks of material – predominantly of acid igneous rock which has solidified within the volcanic pipe and then been brecciated

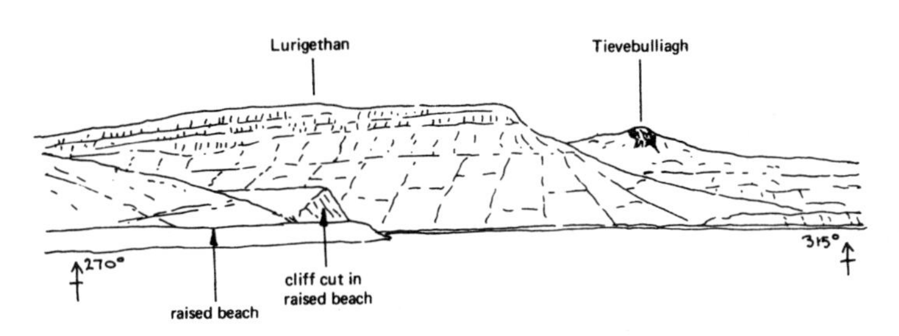

Fig. 44. *Field sketch of the features of No. 104.*

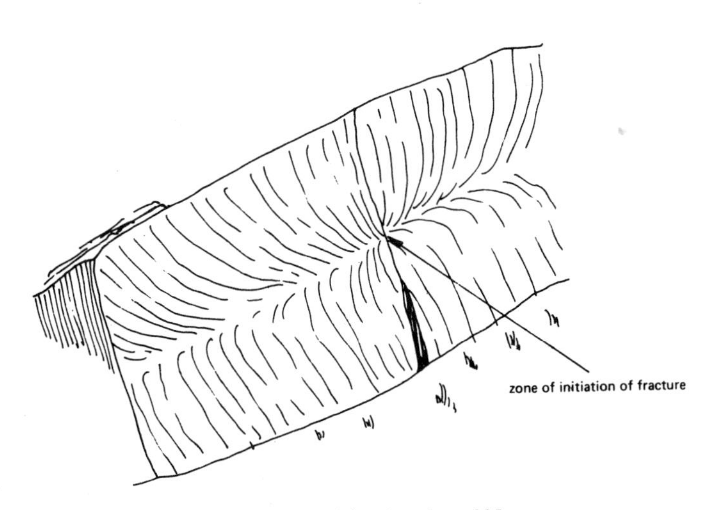

Fig. 45. *Sketch of the joint plane of No. 105.*

and blown out – embedded in a finer grained groundmass. A rough alignment of the larger fragments indicates the bedding. In the welded tuff the alignment is very strong; the larger fragments, or shards, have been flattened, while still hot and plastic, by the weight of the overlying tuff. The groundmass was also hot, and recrystallized on settling to weld the rock together. It is also darker in colour than in the non-welded tuff.

Within a single welded tuff flow, a sequence can often be made out (Fig. 46). The base is usually rubbly and non-welded, while the welded zone follows a few metres above. Welding dies out gradually again in the upper part of the flow, to give a non-welded top (sometimes eroded by succeeding flows or sedimentary rocks). It should be noted that a thin flow may not have any welded zone, and that flattening may occur without any accompanying welding.

Fig. 46. *Vertical section through a typical welded tuff.*

No. 108 **Tuff Dyke. Lower Carboniferous.** *St. Monance, Fife, Scotland.*

Thin bedded shales and limestones of the Lower Carboniferous are here intruded by a dyke of fine agglomerate, or tuff. Infilling the dyke is a breccia of basalt and sedimentary rock fragments, carried into position by high gas pressure. The material probably came from the upper part of a nearby volcanic vent.

No. 109 **Waterlain tuffs.** *L'Aber, Presqu'île de Crozon, Brittany, France.*

Volcanic debris, when it falls on water, forms a deposit which is much more evenly banded and sorted than a subaerial tuff. The smaller particles will sink at varying rates, and will be further moved by bottom currents before being finally deposited. Hence, the tuff may show good bedding and sorting, and sedimentary structures such as current bedding and ripple marking can occur. The larger debris, including angular blocks of lava and sometimes rounded bombs (which solidified in flight), will fall quickly to the sea or lake floor, perhaps sinking into the sediment on which they fall. Some of these features can be seen in this tuff: most blocks are angular, though the largest is rounded, and there are two coarse tuffs, separated by a fine layer about 1 cm thick. This may have been reworked by currents, before the eruption responsible for the second tuff.

Nos 110 and 112 **Volcanic neck and associated dyke.** *Ship Rock, New Mexico, U.S.A.*

The weathered remnants of a volcano are nowhere more dramatically displayed than here, where the resistant plug or neck towers above the landscape. The neck is infilled with tuff-breccia, the hardened pyroclastic material which was formed in the upper parts of the volcanic pipe. The surrounding country rock is a Cretaceous shale. A system of radiating dykes is centered on the pipe, standing out above the desert as a series of hogsback ridges (No. 112). It should be noted that nothing remains of the cone-shaped volcano which stood out above the landscape at the time of eruption: this has long been eroded away, together with the land surface on which it was developed (Fig. 47).

No. 111 **Agglomerate. Elie Harbour vent, Lower Carboniferous.** *Fife, Scotland.*

These coarse ashes and blocks were ejected, principally as already solid material, from an adjacent vent, to fall as a scree-like accumulation of material. A very crude layering, caused by fluctuations in the volcanic activity, is reflected in the undulations of the surface of the

Fig. 47. *Reconstruction of the Ship Rock volcano, after J. Shelton (Nos 110, 112).*

outcrop, though little fluctuation of grain size can be seen.

No. 113 **Volcanic neck. Tertiary rhyolite in Cretaceous sandstone.** *Chisos Mountains, Big Bend National Park, Texas, U.S.A.*

Looking remarkably like a tree, this is a small volcanic plug or neck, not more than about 5m in diameter, intruded through poorly bedded white sandstones. The rhyolite infilling the neck is strongly flow-banded; it also contains a xenolith of country rock, at a height level with that of the head of the figure. As in the Corriegills pitchstone (No. 122) the flowage was extremely viscous and toothpaste-like; but here the 'paste' was frozen in the neck of the tube.

Nos 114–118 **Tertiary Basalt Lavas.** *The Giant's Causeway region, Co. Antrim, N. Ireland.*

The world-famous exposures of Tertiary lavas of the Giant's Causeway are part of the extensive igneous activity which commenced in northern Britain in the Eocene, and continues today in Iceland. The first flows poured out on a land surface of Chalk (No. 115), irregular on a small scale but generally flat, and covered with a thin soil. These flows eventually reached a thickness of some hundreds of metres, though individual flows were thin, with widely spaced, rather irregular, joints. Extrusion of these earlier sequences (the Lower Basalts) was followed by a prolonged period of quiescence, during which there was deep subaerial weathering, reducing the upper flows to a tropical lateritic soil (the Interbasaltic Bed, Nos 115 and 116). Weathering proceeded inwards from the joints of the basalt, to leave spheroidal cores furthest from the joint planes as the last of the basalt to be attacked. The basalt was altered first to a brown colour, as iron oxide was formed; the grey banding was caused by further decomposition to *lithomarge*, a hydrous iron and aluminium silicate; finally all the silica was removed in places to leave a red-coloured clay of iron and aluminium oxides, the *laterite*. This was formerly quarried and mined for smelting, and to produce pigments, but it is no longer a viable operation as the laterite is too thin to mine on a large scale. River systems also cut valleys in the surface, and vegetation was established.

When eruptions resumed, the first flow both filled in the valleys and hollows, and spread out over the higher plateau-like ground. Within the valleys, the pool of thicker basalt cooled slowly and evenly, forming well-developed columns each perpendicular to the underlying land surface. The columns develop during shrinkage within the cooling lava, ideally forming six-sided columns, though with a range from four to ten sides (Nos 114 and 118). In addition joints across the columns are formed, with a slight doming either upwards or downwards (Fig. 48).

At the Causeway, a gully system trending across the present-day coastline was infilled in this manner, and is now partially exhumed by modern coastal erosion: the gully infills of columnar basalt form the reefs of the Causeway itself. Along the cliffs, irregularities on this surface are reflected in variations in the first flow of the Middle Basalts.

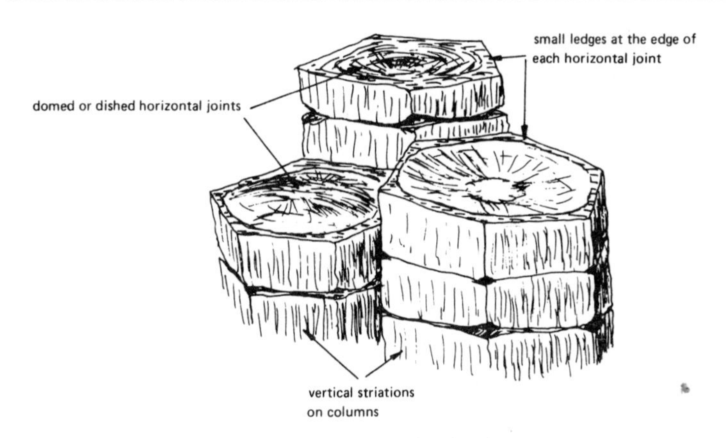

Fig. 48. *Some features of basalt columns.*

No. 114 **Section in the Lower Basalts, Interbasaltic Bed, and middle Basalts.** *The Amphitheatre, Giant's Causeway region.*

The massively jointed exposure to the lower left is of the Lower Basalts, which pass up into the Interbasaltic Bed above the path. Three flows of Middle Basalts are visible. The first is very irregular in thickness and in the development of columns, reflecting the irregular surface onto which it was extruded. In the second flow well developed columns pass up into more irregular and massive ones, which contrast with the thin and irregular columns developed at this horizon in the lower flow. The third flow caps the cliff at the top right.

No. 115 **Lower Basalts resting on Chalk.** *Ballymagarry Quarry, Giant's Causeway region.*

The lower cliff is cut in Chalk, dipping very gently away from the observer, in which the flint horizons are fairly distinct. The top of the Chalk, the early Tertiary land surface, is slightly irregular, and the joints in the overlying basalt tend to be perpendicular to it. The Chalk in the left centre of the picture, partially covered by grass, is not bedded, but is rubbly and crumbling: it is a fossil scree infilling an old swallow hole.

No. 116 **Interbasaltic Bed and base of the Middle Basalts.** *Craigahulliar Quarry, Giant's Causeway region*

The Interbasaltic Bed was here covered by a thick mass of vegetation, some of it in swampy pools. This was charred and crushed by the hot lava above, and now forms a cinder bed, in which recognizable cones and wood can be found. The lava itself has a fine-grained and rubbly base, full of small steam bubbles, and passes up into a more massive basalt.

No. 117 **Spheroidal weathering. Interbasaltic Bed.** *Port Reostan, Giant's Causeway region.*

In this close-up, various stages in the tropical weathering of basalt can be traced in the various colours, ranging from brown, through grey, to reds and purples. The closely spaced joints are probably also a consequence of this weathering, sincc they are not found in the unweathered basalts.

No. 118 **Columnar Basalt.** *The Grand Causeway.*

The columns are here seen to perfection (Fig. 48) in the thickest part of the first flow of the Middle Basalts. The vertical joints are all perfectly parallel, and the majority are six-sided. The domed or dished horizontal joints sometimes have a narrower completely horizontal ledge around them, while on the column edges they tend to curve upwards (note the joint about 30cm below the hammer).

No. 119 **Pillow lavas. Ballantrae Igneous Series.** *Downan Point, Ayrshire, Scotland.*

A number of spilite flows are exposed on the beach platform at this locality, dipping inland at a high angle. The pillows, however, show that the upper surface of the flow lay to the left, and that the sequence is therefore overturned. They interlock in such a way that their original upper surfaces tended to be convex, while their lower surfaces accommodated their shape to that of the underlying pillows (Fig. 49). This demonstrates that each pillow was plastic when coming to rest after extrusion, but rapidly became rigid and resisted the pressure of succeeding pillows. Little material can be seen here between the pillows: it is a softer basaltic tuff, and has been largely eroded away on the outcrop surface.

The pillow lavas are associated with hyaloclastite breccias, formed of angular blocks of spilite, some recognizably from fractured pillows, in a matrix of finer spilitic material. Much of this breccia is formed by explosive activity caused by the boiling of sea water in contact with the pillows.

The Ballantrae Igneous Series contains red cherts, black shales and basic igneous intrusions in addition to the spilites. It has been interpreted as a piece of ocean floor, thrust onto continental crust.

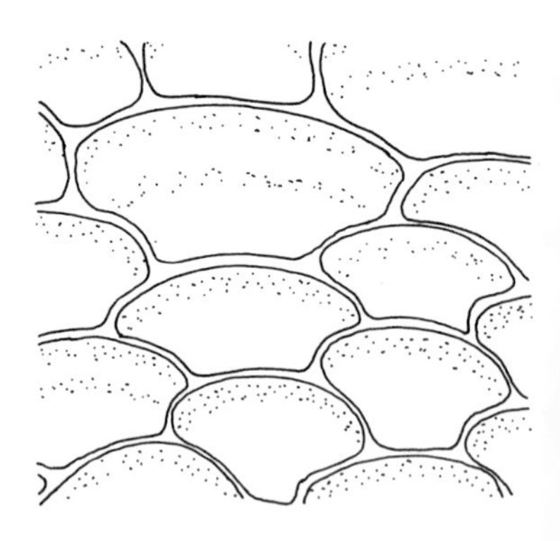

Fig. 49. *Idealized section through a pillow lava sequence, showing the shaping of successive pillows to those beneath (No. 119).*

No. 120 **Pillow lavas with interstitial limestone. Lower Ordovician.** *Lostmarc'h, Presqu'île de Crozon, Brittany, France.*

These pillow lavas dip at a high angle to the left, and are unusual in that the voids between the pillows are filled with a pure grey limestone. Crinoid stem fragments and corals are common fossils in the limestones, and indicate a shallow water origin for both the limestone and the pillows. Such a geological setting is very different from the (presumed) deep sea origin of many pillow lavas, such as those of Downan Point (No. 119).

No. 121 **Jointing in granite. Land's End Granite.** *Land's End, Cornwall, England.*

The granite cliffs of Land's End, so well known to holidaymakers, form a good example of the jointing developed in igneous rocks. A large igneous body, cooling slowly and evenly, generally develops an evenly crystalline texture, often without any preferred orientation of the crystals. Joints may therefore develop in any direction, without the influence of any pre-existing structure, such as bedding, flow banding, or schistosity. The joints which develop in such rocks are usually a) vertical, in two or three directions, and b) parallel to the ground surface. The first type of joint may reflect shrinkage (cf. columnar lavas, p. 190), or regional tension. The second type may result from relief of pressure when the overburden is stripped off the rock: these joints often follow the irregularities of the ground surface. It has also been suggested that the converse is true, that the joints are due to tectonic events, and have subsequently controlled the erosion.

No. 122 **Flowfolds in pitchstone.** *Corriegills, Isle of Arran, Scotland.*

Acid igneous material does not flow easily, and one can liken it to stiff toothpaste. It moves slowly, and cools to form flows of limited extent, and similar characteristics are evident in thin dykes and sills. During flowage, folds such as those shown here form due to the drag of the viscous material; they may be compared to the folds found in some high grade metamorphic rocks (cf. No. 149). The light coloured layer shows ptygmatic folding, and indicates that it is formed of material which was more resistant. Broken surfaces show the characteristic fracture of the rock: it is so fine grained, or even noncrystalline or glassy, that it has this pitch-like appearance.

This is one of a number of thin intrusions, of Tertiary age, which cooled extremely rapidly. It has been famous since the beginning of the nineteenth century.

Nos 123 and 124 **Hutton's Contact. Teschenite Sill intruded into Old Red Sandstones.** *Salisbury Crags, Edinburgh, Scotland.*

This sill of teschenite (a variety of dolerite rich in sodic minerals) is intruded into pink and white sandstones of the Upper Old Red Sandstones. The bulk of the sill has cooled slowly, and shows good columnar jointing. Towards the base and top the magma was chilled against the country rock, giving a finer grained rock without columnar joints. At the lower contact discordant relations can be observed where the sill transgresses the bedding, with a small tongue of igneous material frozen in the act of penetrating a bedding plane, forcing upwards and bending the strata above it.

This outcrop is historically important in that here Hutton, a Scotsman who was one of the founders of geology, demonstrated the intrusive nature of the sill. It had been maintained by a school of geologists called the Neptunists that such rocks were laid down on the sea floor, like other sediments, while the Plutonists, led by Hutton, claimed that they were formed from molten magma, as were lava flows.

Nos 125 and 126 **Contact metamorphism at the top of a dolerite sill.** *Ramore Head, Portrush, Co. Antrim, N. Ireland.*

No. 125 shows the contact at the top of a thick sill of dolerite with the overlying sediments. These are of Lias Clay, ordinarily unconsolidated grey clays, which elsewhere in Co. Antrim cause landslips and mud glaciers (cf. those of No. 34). Here, the clays (No. 125) have been baked or hornfelsed to an extremely hard and brittle porcellanite, very like chert in appearance and hardness. Although the contact generally follows the bedding of the clays, it is quite irregular on a small scale, the hornfels and dolerite interfingering in a manner which suggests that the clays were almost rendered molten by the heat. The grain size of the dolerite also becomes finer towards the contact.

This outcrop figured prominently in the geological controversy at the end of the eighteenth century between the Neptunists and the Plutonists or Vulcanists (cf. No. 123). The Neptunists failed to appreciate the significance of this contact, and linking together the sill and the hornfels, regarded both as 'igneous' rock, in which were undoubted ammonites (No. 126); proof of its marine origin.

No. 127 **Roof of granite sill.** *Rinsey Cove, south of Helston, Cornwall, England.*

The upper contact of a granite sill, intruded into horizontally foliated hornfelsed phyllites, can be seen at the top of the picture (Fig. 50). The phyllite is spotted with andalusite and tourmaline crystals, while a skin about 2cm thick at the actual contact is baked to a flinty rock, purple in colour. The uppermost 7cm of the granite is fine grained, chilled against the sediments above. Beneath is a layer, about 15cm thick, with conspicuous feldspar crystals, while below is a finer even grained granite which forms the bulk of the intrusion. The large feldspar crystals of the central layer probably grew slowly downwards as pendants hanging from the chilled roof of the intrusion, expanding from a small attached apex, while the magma beneath was still molten.

No. 128 **The North Star Dyke. Tertiary Dolerite intruding Lower Carboniferous Coal Measures.** *Ballycastle, Co. Antrim, N. Ireland.*

The North Star Dyke is a dolerite of Tertiary age, intruded into gently inclined sandstones of Lower Carboniferous age, along a north–south fault. The jointing within the dyke is characteristic: vertical joints both parallel and perpendicular to the dyke walls, and near horizontal joints also perpendicular to the dyke walls.

In the distance is Rathlin Island, whose cliffs are formed of the white Chalk overlain by flows of basalt.

No. 129 **Granite dykes.** *Porth Meor, Cornwall, England.*

Two dykes of granite, part of the large Land's End Granite nearby, are intruded into contact metamorphosed slates. The latter contain the mineral tourmaline, and are extremely hard and flinty. The earlier dyke is fine grained, and has slightly irregular margins which suggest that the slate was somewhat plastic at the time of intrusion. The later dyke, darker in colour and porphyritic, clearly cuts the earlier and has straighter margins. The earlier dyke is displaced along it, but it is not clear if this displacement occurred during intrusion (lubrication by the magma aiding the movement) or by faulting of the first dyke, followed by injection of the second along the fault plane.

No. 130 **Basic dykes. Dolerite dykes intruded into the Pre-Cambrian Rosslare Gneisses.** *Kilmore Quay, Co. Wexford, Eire.*

The country rocks are highly metamorphosed sediments, in which the only structure to be seen is an irregular mineral segregation, which may not reflect the original bedding. A dark band of rock towards the background was probably intruded as a basic dyke, and its farther contact appears sharp against the gneisses. It too has been metamorphosed, and contains bands of mineral segregations. In the foreground a later basic dyke cuts both the gneisses and the earlier dyke. It has sharp contacts against them, but is too fine grained throughout to show chilling visible

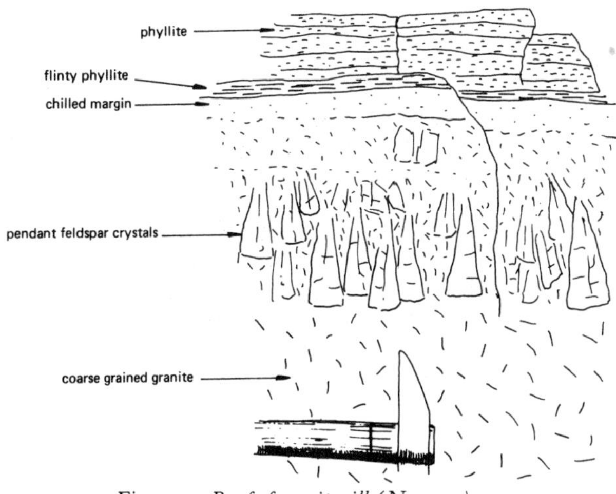

Fig. 50. *Roof of granite sill (No. 127).*

in the photograph. Note the block of gneiss just above the hammer head, which has been frozen just in the act of being plucked off the country rock by the intrusion; it now forms a xenolith. Joint planes are irregular in this heterogeneous rock mass.

No. 131 **Cone sheets intruded into Jurassic limestones.** *Kilchoan, Ardnamurchan, Argyllshire, Scotland.*

The Tertiary igneous centre of the Ardnamurchan peninsula is one of the best developed in the British Isles, and individual cone sheets are well exposed in coastal exposures around the peninsula. Two cone sheets of dolerite are present here, dipping to the left at 50–60°. They are about 1.6km from the centre of the system, and thus the apex of the cone is about 2km down from the surface (Fig. 51). The sheet in the foreground is cut by a vertical dyke running across the photograph; like the cone sheets, it is of dolerite, weathering to a brown colour. It is one of a series of later dykes connected to the same centre, but radiating out from it.

No. 132 **Granite cutting hornfels.** *Grande Etaquerel, Jersey, Channel Islands.*

On the left, banded hornfels dips steeply downwards (eastwards) towards the white coloured granite. The granite/hornfels contact, though very clean cut, is not a plane, for it is slightly irregular in detail. The red-shirted geologist is examining a tongue of dark coloured hornfels, extending nearly to the floor of the quarry and surrounded on both sides by granite. The coarse grained granite does not show any significant diminution in grain size towards the contacts. It was intruded into the Jersey Shales, sediments of turbidite

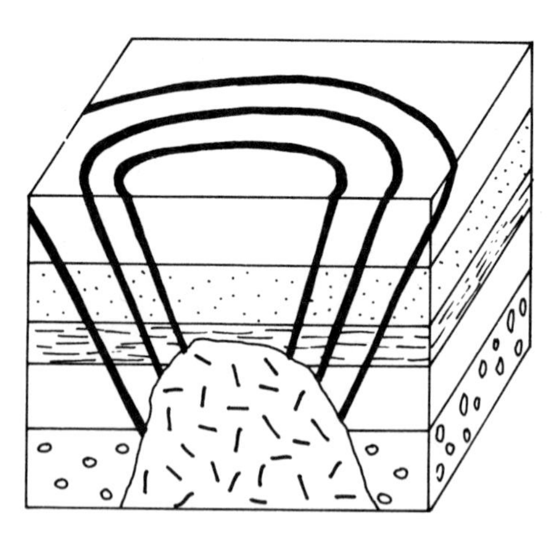

Fig. 51. *Cone sheets related to an intrusion at depth.*

facies, thermally metamorphosing them into hornfelses. The tongue of hornfels is part of a block that was being wedged off near the roof of the granite intrusion.

No. 133 **Porphyritic Granite. Outer Dartmoor Granite.** *Blackstone Rock, Devonshire, England.*

This close-up of a granite shows large phenocrysts of orthoclase feldspar, set in an equigranular groundmass. The phenocrysts crystallized first, as is shown by their rectangular (lath-shaped) outlines. The surrounding groundmass is composed of smaller feldspar crystals (pale cream), biotite (black) and quartz (glassy grey). Close to the scale is a patch rich in biotite, which may have been a xenolith of non-granitic material, rich in ferro-magnesian minerals, now almost completely digested.

No. 134 **Layered Gabbro.** *St. Peter Port Gabbro, Richmond Corner, Guernsey, Channel Islands.*

A rhythmic banding is picked out by the dark hornblende crystals, set in a matrix of greenish feldspars. These two minerals comprise the bulk of the rock, to the exclusion of pyroxene. The banding indicates alternation of conditions during the cooling of the igneous body, perhaps temperature fluctuations, or injections of extra magma.

No. 135 **Greisen veins in granite.** *Cligga Head, Cornwall, England.*

The granite has conspicuous tabular crystals of feldspar, set in a matrix of quartz and subordinate dark minerals. Two tin-bearing veins are surrounded by a zone of soaking, or pneumatolitic, diffusion, of tin-bearing minerals into the granite. The resulting association is known as a greisen. Horizontal jointing in the granite is only well developed in the greisen zones. It may have been developed as the level of erosion approached that of the present day (p. 193).

No. 136 **Coarse gabbro. Ballantrae Igneous Series.** *Lendalfoot, Ayrshire, Scotland.*

The rock illustrates well the coarsely crystalline texture of a slowly cooled igneous rock, in this case a basic rock formed of white plagioclase feldspars and dark augite. Neither mineral shows good crystal outlines, suggesting that the minerals grew at the same time, the growing crystals eventually interfering with one another to produce an interlocking pattern.

No. 137 **Intrusion Breccia. Granophyre intruding gabbro.** *Grigadale, Ardnamurchan, Scotland.*

Two stages in the process of stoping during intrusion can be seen in this exposure. To the left is the country rock, itself an intrusion of dark gabbro. It is penetrated by light coloured veins of medium grained granophyre, representing acid magma frozen in the act of penetrating cracks in the gabbro. The process proceeds with the removal of blocks of the country rock from the contact to form xenoliths in the intruding rock. This stage is seen on the right, where the xenoliths are so numerous as to form an intrusion breccia. Here the angular blocks, both of gabbro and finer grained dolerite are set in a cement of granophyre.

No. 138 **Contact between igneous rocks. Granite intruding diorite.** *Baie de Pequeries, Guernsey, Channel Islands.*

The older rock is a dark diorite, rich in greenish hornblende, together with biotite, as the dark minerals, and plagioclase feldspar together with a little quartz forming the light component. The intruding granite contains conspicuous orthoclase feldspar laths, and very few dark minerals. The contact between the two rocks is unusual in its crenulate appearance, and in the dark rim formed against it in the diorite. It has been suggested that the diorite was still liquid, or nearly so, when the granite was intruded, but that the two magmas did not mix. The rim contains hornblende and orthoclase feldspar, in contrast to the plagioclase of the bulk of the diorite; this is evidence of some reaction and diffusion between the two magmas.

No. 139 **Phyllites. Cullenstown Group, late Pre-Cambrian.** *Cullenstown, Co. Wexford, Eire.*

Both the crystalline and structural state of these rocks are characteristic of low grade phyllites. The green colour is due principally to chlorite. A sandstone, or psammite, is interbedded with shales, metamorphosed to phyllites. The psammite is graded, with a sharp lower contact and a more gradational upper one. This may indicate that the under surface was the original bottom of the bed (cf. No. 35) and could prove a very valuable clue to the structure of the region. The inclined anticline and syncline are associated with an

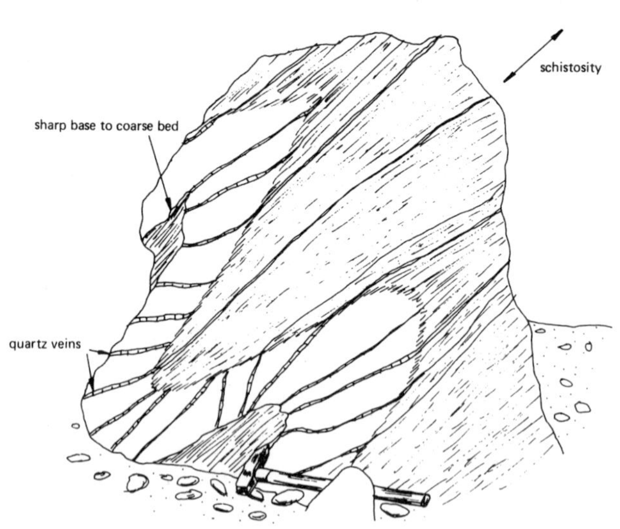

Fig. 52. *Folds in phyllites (No. 139).*

axial plane foliation, which fans from the cores of the folds (Fig. 52). The foliation is weaker towards the coarser base of the psammite. Very thin quartz veins are injected along the foliation of the phyllite (further metamorphism of the rock to a higher grade would cause these to appear as siliceous layers, easily mistaken for original sedimentary layers.)

No. 140 **Syncline in low grade schists. South Stack Series, Pre-Cambrian.** *Porth-y-post, Anglesey, Wales.*

These rocks are low grade chloritic schists, very similar to those of the Cullenstown Group in Ireland (No. 139), but are more severely deformed. Apparent laminations at the bottom right and top left are metamorphic in origin, while between these regions an anticline and syncline can still be made out, with their original bedding. Development of the foliation has not yet destroyed the coarser graded beds, and as at Cullenstown the sharp bases of these beds are still identifiable.

No. 141 **Folded phyllites. Mylor Beds, ?Devonian.** *Porthleven, Cornwall, England.*

Well-laminated sandstones, siltstones and shales have been metamorphosed to phyllites, and demonstrate two phases of folding. Well-developed similar folds, with axial planes dipping to the right, exhibit some thickening in the fold hinges. Close inspection of some of the beds, particularly just above the hammer head, shows an earlier set of isoclinal folds, now refolded by the later ones.

No. 142 **Refolded psammitic bands in schists.** *Dalradian, Linsfort, Co. Donegal, Eire.*

Near-vertical layers of psammite are interbedded with schists, which have an axial plane foliation parallel to the bedding. Isoclinal folds are present. The second period of folding has taken place along inclined axes (Fig. 53), and the associated axial plane foliation can be seen destroying the original vertical foliation, as the platy minerals are recrystallized in the new direction. Note that the *axes* of the two periods of folding are approximately parallel.

No. 143 **Boudinaged quartz vein. Birrimian Series, Pre-Cambrian.** *Takoradi, Ghana.*

This predominantly basic gneiss is evenly banded, except for the line of lenticular quartz masses or *boudins*. These are, in fact, rod-like in three dimensions and once formed a continuous sheet of quartz. Stretching parallel to the layering at first caused the sheet to 'pinch' along a series of parallel lines, and eventually to rupture.

No. 144 **Interference patterns in gneiss. Pre-Cambrian.** *Norway.*

Two sets of folds, at right angles to one another, have caused the interference pattern seen here, though it is not possible to establish which is earlier. The more prominent set trends across the picture, forming plunging folds. Two basin structures are present further to the right, caused by the interference of the weaker folds, trending away from the observer (Fig. 54).

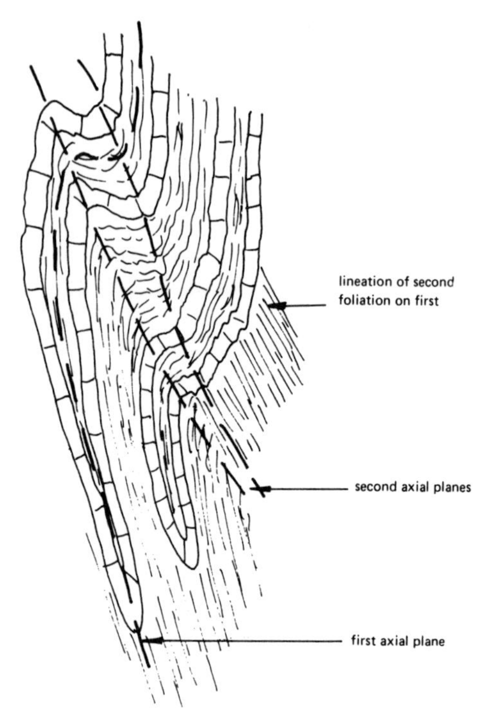

Fig. 53. *Refolded isoclinal folds (No. 142).*

No. 145 **Quartz-feldspar schist.** *Dalradian, Cushendun, Co. Antrim, N. Ireland.*

In this medium grade schist, the folded layering is probably purely metamorphic, the minerals having separated into bands parallel to the foliation. Quartz bands may have been former quartz veins (as in No. 139); brick red layers are rich in feldspar, while the darker layers are composed of biotite and feldspar. Later quartz veins cut sharply across the metamorphic banding.

No. 146 **Metamorphosed turbidites. Pre-Cambrian.** *Takoradi, Ghana.*

A turbidite sequence (cf. No. 35) is here metamorphosed to garnet grade, to form an alternation of garnet mica schists and psammites, but has otherwise suffered little distortion. Garnet crystals are conspicuously developed in the fine-grained tops to the turbidites, and form a grading themselves but in the reverse sense to that of the sediments, i.e. the garnet size increasing with

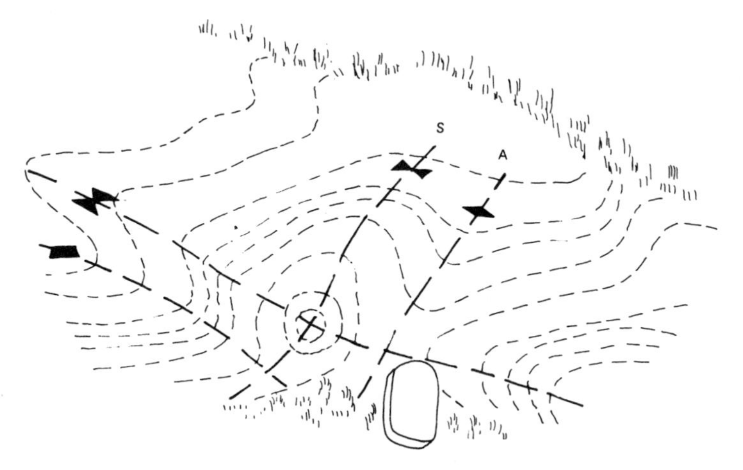

Fig. 54. *The fold axes of No. 144.* S *syncline.* A *anticline.*

decreasing grain size. The brown line is the outcrop of a joint plane, with a rusty staining caused by limonite precipitation during weathering.

No. 147 **Garnet mica schist. Pre-Cambrian.** *St. Cast, Brittany, France.*

Reddish brown garnet crystals, up to 10mm in diameter, dominate the mineralogy of this medium grade schist. They are *porphyroblasts*, analogous to porphyritic crystals in igneous rock (e.g. No. 133), but they have grown during the course of metamorphism while the rock remained in a solid state. The rock also has quartz grains up to 2mm in diameter. These, in contrast to the garnets, are likely to be original sedimentary grains, though they may have grown in size during metamorphism (microscopic investigation would be necessary to resolve this question). The rest of the rock is composed of the micas biotite and muscovite, the former predominating.

If the quartz grains are original, the sediment deposited will have been composed of them, together with a greater proportion of clay minerals. These may have been present as mud, but equally could have been fragments of mudstone, shale, turbidite, or even schist from an earlier metamorphic cycle.

No. 148 **Banded migmatites. Concordia Granite intruded into Rietberg Biotite Schist. Pre-Cambrian.** *Nababeep, Namaqualand, Cape Province, South Africa.*

Dark basic gneiss alternates with acid granitic material, described as intrusive into the gneiss, but more probably in the process of being sweated out, and becoming liquid, as in No. 150. Of interest is the small fault in the left hand band of gneiss, which offsets banding within it, but not its boundaries against the acid gneiss. The gneiss must have been faulted in a period of brittle deformation before the acid bands were formed. These, above the end of the scale, contain dark streaks, which undulate in a manner that suggests ripple marks in a sediment.

No. 149 **Migmatites. Pre-Cambrian.** *Near Tupper Lake, Adirondacks, New York State, U.S.A.*

The vertical face has been exposed by blasting, the lighter coloured vertical stripes marking the site of the shot holes drilled from the top of the face. The country rock is a dark even grained gneiss, with a foliation dipping gently to the left. The pink rock is an acid injection rich in a pink orthoclase feldspar. Near the hammer it is injected as sheets between the bands of gneiss (*lit-par-lit* or bed-by-bed injection). Above, however, there is so much material injected that the gneiss is being fragmented into detached blocks, or xenoliths.

No. 150 **Migmatite. Pre-Cambrian.** *St. Jacut, Brittany, France.*

Acidic material has here been frozen as it was becoming mobile, and presumably molten. Much of the exposure consists of biotite-rich gneiss interbanded with granular acid gneiss, with complex folding. Here and there the acid material transgresses the foliation of the basic gneiss, forming masses such as the one on which the pen is resting. It contains a few small enclaves of basic gneiss, which may be described as xenoliths in what is now granite (Fig. 55).

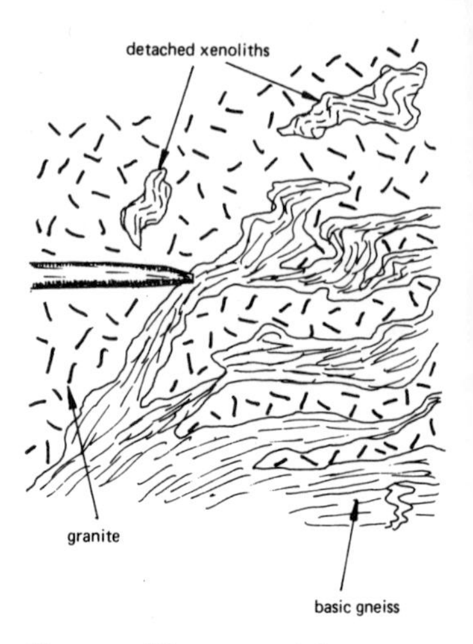

Fig. 55. *The texture of the migmatite in No. 150.*

No. 151 **Pegmatite vein in gneiss. Pre-Cambrian.** *North of Le Conquet, Pays de Leon, Brittany, France.*

Foliation in the gneiss is defined by crude planes rich in biotite, separated by bands of quartz and feldspar. The pegmatite vein clearly cross-cuts this foliation, and is much later in origin: it may have been derived from a neighbouring igneous intrusion. It is filled with an intergrowth of cream feldspar and glassy quartz crystals, reaching lengths of 4–5 cm.

No. 152 **Dendritic marks on bedding plane. Solenhofen Limestone, Upper Jurassic.** *Solenhofen, West Germany.*

The photograph is of a bedding plane in the Solenhofen Limestone, an extremely pure and fine grained limestone from southern Germany. It is world famous for its unique and well preserved suite of fossils, including the reptile/bird *Archaeopteryx*. It is also famous as a lithographic stone, that is as engraved stone for use in the printing industry.

Two phases of dendritic marks are present, both deposited from water percolating along the bedding planes from joint planes visible at the bottom of the photograph. Notice that the colour of the two sets of marks is different, reflecting different mineral composition of the ground water in each phase.

No. 153 **Deformation due to soil creep. Lower Silurian.** *Pont Erwyd, Dyfed (Cardiganshire), Wales.*

The cleaved slates on the side of an old quarry strike towards the observer, and dip in the same direction as the hillside, but much more steeply. These are the optimum conditions for deformation by soil creep down the hillside to disrupt the bedding or cleavage in the weathered zone, and a deflection or *terminal curvature* through 90° has occurred. The blocks above the map case are spoil from former quarrying operations.

Nos 154 and 155 **Hand drilling or augering.** *Site of post glacial lake, near Llandyssul, Dyfed (Cardiganshire), Wales.*

Hand drilling is seen here being used to obtain a sample of former lake sediments. In this case the screw end used to obtain rock samples has been replaced by a box which can cut and retain a sample of the unconsolidated sediment. The drillers are standing on light metal ladders, which provide support on the marshy floor of the swamp. The core obtained shows a transition from soft grey clays to peat.

No. 156 **The sample field map**

The area shown is of an anticline in uppermost Ordovician rocks in Wales, mapped on the scale of six inches to one mile (nearly 1 : 10,000). The topographic map does not show contours, but the anticline forms an elongate hill in the sandstones and slumped beds, while the shales are softer and outcrop in depressions. The two faults which cross the anticline also form valleys. Crag symbols on the map indicate the larger rock outcrops, but they are not completely accurate in position and are to some extent stylized. The boundaries of outcrops are shown as black dotted lines, not green, as this has simplified the reproduction of the map. The blue feature symbols are more accurate reflections of the topographic changes caused by the underlying rocks, and have been drawn partly from field observations and partly from aerial photographs. In the very well exposed sandstones not all the features have been drawn in; they are too closely crowded together. Other topographical features have been added to the base map, in particular the large quarry beside the old tramway, which was not opened until after the last revision of the map.

Geologically the map is very straightforward. The anticline plunges gently to the north, while to the south the plunge decreases and it becomes horizontal. The two faults downthrow to the south, and also offset the anticlinal axis slightly. They are marked by old adits and shafts, driven in search of lead ore in the fault breccias. The oldest rocks of the area, the slumped sandstones, are the most difficult aspect of the area to interpret. On the western limb of the anticline they are succeeded by 18m of sandstones, while on the eastern limb there are over 40m of sandstones. Since the top of the sandstones maps out as a single horizon – parallel everywhere to the bedding planes in the sandstones and in the overlying shales, the contact between the slumped beds and the sandstones must be strongly diachronous (Fig. 56). Vertical east–west joints are well developed, particularly in the sandstones (No. 105), and have been plotted on a rose diagram (Fig. 10).

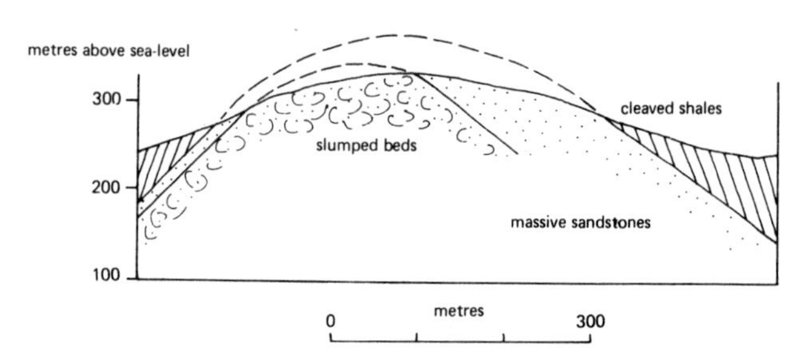

Fig. 56. *E–W cross-section through the area of the sample field map (No. 156), just north of Carn Owen.*

IV LOCALITIES FOR FIELD WORK

8 SOURCES OF INFORMATION

Publications of the Institute of Geological Sciences

The prime function of the Institute of Geological Sciences (formerly the Geological Survey of Great Britain), is the production of geological maps and the assessment of mineral resources of all kinds. Whilst its publications are invaluable for their overall coverage of the geology, they do not give specific advice as to routes for field excursions, etc. These, however, can be worked out from the study of the appropriate official maps and memoirs.

However, it must be appreciated that, whilst the Geological Survey has published maps on the scale of 1:63,360 (the 'one-inch' maps), now being replaced by the 1:50,000 scale, for the whole of Great Britain and for parts of northern Ireland, some of these maps date from many years ago. Parts of the Lake District, Central Wales and East Anglia have not been officially surveyed since the beginning of the present century. Revision of the earlier mapping has been concentrated on the areas of greatest economic importance (the coalfields, ironstone fields, etc.) or of population density. It is therefore always wise to look at the statement below the bottom left-hand corner of the map which gives the date of the survey. As indication of the time needed to carry out thorough geological mapping, it will be noted that each sheet (usually covering an area of 18 by 12 miles, but larger in Scotland) has normally occupied two or more surveyors over a period of two years or more.

Descriptive memoirs have been published for most of the maps. Those for the earlier sheets tend to be brief or several maps may be combined together in a district memoir. Those for the more recent sheets are considerably longer, usually giving detailed accounts of the exposures seen by the surveyors. Clearly, the older the memoir, the less likelihood of the exposures described in it being open now. Also over the years there have been improvements not only in the technique of geological mapping, but also in appreciating the significance of certain geological features.

For example, it is only in the past thirty years that the extent of Head deposits (p. 35), the areas of cambering (p. 36) and of landslipping (p. 26) have been shown by a special symbol and colour on the official maps, also much more attention is now paid than formerly to structural geology, especially to minor structures (p. 40). The absence of such features on the older maps does not necessarily mean that they were not present on the ground. The policy at the time of the survey was not to record them.

The 1:10,560 ('6 inch') field slips from which the '1 inch' maps have been drawn are unique manuscripts, and therefore, special permission is needed before they can be consulted. Fair copies of the field slips with a selection of the field observations on them, are, however, available for consultation by anyone, as are all the other publications and maps of the Institute in the
Library of the Geological
Survey Museum,
Exhibition Road,
South Kensington,
London SW7,

or in the libraries of the Scottish Office,
19 Grange Terrace,
Edinburgh EH9 2LF

and at
Ring Road,
Halton,
Leeds LS15 8TQ.

Publications of the Geological Societies and Other Bodies

The journals and proceedings of a number of geological societies contain many papers describing the geology, or specialist aspects of the geology, of specific areas, together often with the reports of field meetings or geological excursions. There may be no recent official maps or memoirs for some of these areas. But whilst the Institute of Geological Sciences keeps an index of all its publications, so that all the official accounts of a particular locality can be quickly located, this cannot be done for the relevant communications that may be scattered through the different journals, proceedings, etc. It is true that some societies issue at irregular intervals detailed indices to their particular journal, but this is not a regular practice and such indices appear only spasmodically. Areal bibliographies are to be found in the series of British Regional Geology handbooks published by the Stationery Office for the Institute of Geological Sciences, but these are by no means exhaustive and usually do not contain the reports of field meetings.

The now defunct *Welsh Geological Quarterly* published a very useful annotated bibliography and index of geological guides and reports in three parts, which are still obtainable from
A. J. Thomas,
Hon. Secretary,
Geologists' Association,
South Wales Group,
c/o National Museum of Wales,
Cardiff CF1 3NP,
as follows:

Scotland (105 excursions) published in 1967, 20p.
Wales (94 excursions) published in 1968, 20p.
England (530 excursions) published in 1969, 40p.

The prices quoted (in 1975) include postage.

The Geologists' Association publish a series of *Field Guides*, to areas such as South Shropshire, Snowdonia, the Yorkshire Coast, Skye, Isle of Wight, etc. These can be obtained from
The Scientific Anglian,
30/30A St. Benedict's Street,
Norwich,
Norfolk NOR 24J.

In addition the Association also runs a regular programme of field meetings, day, weekend or longer, to localities both within and outside the British Isles. (General Secretary Dr. W. J. French, Geology Dept., Queen Mary College, Mile End Road, London E1 4NS.) Certain of these field meetings are specifically designed for the beginner in geology, including instruction in elementary field mapping, whilst reports of many of them are included in the Association's proceedings. The circulars of the Association, issued at monthly intervals except in the summer, also contain the programme of field and other meetings as well as the address of the secretary of many other geological societies, e.g. Cumberland Geological Society, Yorkshire Geological Society, Edinburgh Geological Society, East Midlands Geological Society, Ipswich Geological Group, The Devonshire Association (Geology Group), etc.

The beginner in geology would be well advised to join either the Geologists' Association or his appropriate local society, so as to receive its publications, to be able to participate in its field meetings, to make useful contacts and in a number of cases to be able to consult its library which may contain survey maps mounted for use in the field.

Another useful body is:
The Association of Teachers of Geology,
Secretary, D. S. Scott, Crewe and Alsager College of Higher Education, Crewe Road, Crewe CW1 1DU.
At its annual conference there is much exchange of information, both formally and informally, on field work, whilst its journal *Geology* contains, in addition to articles on a variety of geological topics and reviews of recently published books, many useful advertisements as regards field equipment, field accommodation and field guides to specific areas.

The Geology and Physiography Section of the Nature Conservancy Council,
Foxhold House,
Thornfold Road,
Crookham Common,
Newbury,
Berkshire,
is not only responsible for the scheduling of Sites of Special Scientific Importance and for presenting the case for geologists when important exposures are under threat from developments of any kind, but also issues a useful series of information circulars. These give details of new exposures, warnings where access has either been refused or has to be applied for through a particular channel, warnings of overhammering of certain exposures, together with lists of motorways, trunk roads and pipeline schemes which may provide informative temporary sections.

Museums are another possible source of information, but unfortunately the position varies greatly up and down the country. There are those museums, including the great national museums such as the Geological Survey Museum and the British Museum (Natural History) in London and the National Museum of Wales in Cardiff, whose staff have the expertise not only to stage fascinating exhibits, but also to provide a geological information service including advice on localities for field work. Yet there are other museums whose staff have little or no appreciation of geology. It is well worth visiting your local museum to find out how much geological help it can provide or if you will have to go elsewhere.

9 SUPPLIERS OF FIELD EQUIPMENT

In the past few years there has been a great increase in the number of shops dealing in minerals, rock polishing equipment, etc. Many of these shops stock geological hammers. Dealers who supply as well as hammers and chisels, more specialist equipment (compass/clinometers, augers, etc.) include:

Gregory Botley,
30 Old Church Street,
Chelsea,
London SW3.

Cutrock Engineering Co.,
35 Ballard's Lane,
London N3.

Whithear Lapidary Co.,
35 Manor Way,
North Harrow HA2 6BZ.

Hammers are also made by
W. Whitehouse & Co.,
Atlas Works,
Newlyn Road,
Cradley Heath,
Warley,
Worcs. B64 6BN.

Chisels are stocked by the majority of ironmongers as cold chisels, and are therefore easily available.

The most widely used compass/clinometer is the Silva Ranger 15TD-CL, one of a range of Silva compasses most of which are stocked by camping and climbing shops, though this model may have to be obtained as a special order.

Scale rules bearing the more widely used map scales can be obtained from shops specializing in drafting and surveying equipment. Alternately, a scale can be made by pasting the scale from the map onto a sheet of cardboard, and covering it with transparent plastic such as that sold for protecting book covers. It may also be useful to include on one side of this the grid for the map. In the case of the British National Grid, which is based on 1-km squares, this will also be the metric scale for the maps. A further useful scale is one worked out in paces, so that they can be directly plotted on the map. It will, of course, be unique to each individual geologist.

A map case can be easily made from sheets of hardboard, bulldog clips to hold the maps, and an outer waterproof cover. An inner transparent cover for the face of the maps is sometimes used also. The size of the case is a matter of preference; too small a case means that the map will have to be folded or cut into small pieces, and this causes problems when working close to the map edges, whilst too large a case becomes inconvenient to carry.

Handlenses are widely available from opticians, chemists, hobby shops, etc. ×10 or ×8 are the most useful sizes, though more elaborate lenses are available offering more than one magnification.

There are basically two types of

pens used for inking in maps, mapping pens and technical pens. Mapping pens, used by dipping them repeatedly into the bottle of ink, are extremely cheap, and with practice will give very fine lines. It may be necessary to try a number of nibs before finding one that gives sufficiently fine lines, but at about 3p per nib (1975) they can be bought by the dozen. At the other end of the scale are technical pens with reservoirs, costing (in 1975) about £1–2 each (e.g. Rapidograph, Standardgraph) which come in a range of sizes producing different thicknesses of line. The thinnest available (0.1mm) is the most useful, but it is very liable to clog if left filled with ink, and it is advisable to empty and clean it each night.

10 PHOTOGRAPHY IN THE FIELD

Virtually every type of camera has been used for taking field photographs, from cheap snapshot cameras to large plate models. There is no doubt that the latter can yield excellent results in skilled hands, but for most purposes the 35mm camera will form the best compromise between portability and technical excellence. It should have at least a variable focus lens, so that close-ups as well as landscapes will be sharp. It is not necessary, however, to have a fast lens or a fast shutter.

Almost all the photographs in this book have been taken with a 35mm reflex camera taking interchangeable lenses, undoubtedly the most convenient instrument for field use. Most such cameras have standard lenses which will focus down to less than 0.5m (the closer the better), while a Macro lens will enable same-size close-ups to be taken without the use of close-up lenses, extension tubes or bellows. A wide-angle lens is useful for working in confined spaces, but not essential.

Exposure calculation presents few problems which are not met within ordinary photography. For colour transparencies, an incident light meter, which measures the intensity of light falling on the subject, will give the best reading of exposure for most subjects. In the absence of a meter, the table supplied with most films will be perfectly adequate, and in unskilled hands may be more reliable than a meter which can be easily used incorrectly. For an important photograph, which cannot easily be retaken, it is worth taking three 'shots' at slightly different exposures.

The depth of field given by a 35mm camera is also useful when taking close-ups. Study of some of the close-ups in this book (e.g. No. 66) will show that even with a 35mm camera parts of the picture will be out of focus ('outside' the depth of field). This zone, within which the image will be acceptably sharp, increases as the lens is closed down, so that a small stop (high stop number) is often essential. However, this means that a longer exposure is necessary, increasing the risk of camera shake. Hence, for some photographs, a tripod may be necessary.

A flash gun, preferably electronic,

is an extremely useful accessory. For colour work, particularly in close-up, it heightens the colour and colour contrast, as well as enabling hand-held shots to be made in dull light, or under overhangs or in deep shadows. A computerized gun will automatically determine the correct exposure, since it controls the amount of flash light emitted by measuring the light returned from the outcrop to the gun and camera. For an ordinary gun, the exposure has to be calculated. Here the exposure table given with the gun is usually based on indoor use, where reflected light from the walls and ceiling is added to direct light from the gun. For outdoor use the exposure calculated from the table should be doubled, by opening up the lens by one stop (e.g. *f*8 instead of *f*11). A flash gun can also be used for fill-in flash, to lighten shadows in an otherwise sunlit picture, though this is not often necessary. A more complicated calculation has to be carried out, and details can be found in a photographic handbook.

Photography in black and white of rock outcrops is in some aspects more difficult than colour photography. Oblique lighting is more often required, to throw shadows which can reveal the form of the rock surface. This is even more important when using a flash gun, as a gun on the camera gives an even illumination of the rock, effectively suppressing any relief on the surface. To overcome this the gun should be moved away from the camera and fired using an extension lead.

INDEX

References to the colour plates are in **bold** type; figure numbers of the line illustrations are in *italics*; text page numbers are in Roman.

Acid bottle, 20
Aeolian bedding, **19**, 155
Agglomerate, 74, 76, **111**, 189–90
Alluvium, *3*, 30
Ammonites, **126**, 194
Angular discordance, **27**, 157
—unconformity, 65, *16*, **18**, 154, *22*
Anticline, **6**, 151, **72**, 170–1, *27*, **76**, 172, *29*
— inclined, **91–3**, 181, *37–8*
Antiform, *3*, 30, 43
Aplite, 79
Arenaceous rocks, 51–3
Argillaceous rocks, 53
Arkose, 52
Ash-flow tuff, 75
Assimilation, 80
Augen-gneiss, 147
Auger, 32, **154–5**, 202

Ballstone, **44**, 163
Banding, *3*, 30
Basalt, **114–8**, 190–2
Batholith, 78
Bauxite, 51
Bedding/cleavage relationship, 41–2, *7*, **78**, 173–4
— contorted, *3*, 30
— convolute, 55, *25*, **40**, 162
— inverted, **21**, 155, **74**, 171
— plane, 21, *1*, **48**, 162
— plane slip, 72
Bone bed, 58–9, **56**, 167
Boss, 78
Boudinage, **143**, 199
Boulder clay, *3*, 30, 50, **11–2**, 152, **14**
Boundaries on geological maps, 28–30, *3*
Breaks in deposition, 65–6, *16*
Breccia, 48–9, **4**, 150, **55**, 167
—hyaloclastite, **119**, 192
— intrusive, **137**, 197
Breccio-conglomerate, **2**, 150
Broken Beds, **53**, 166
Burrows, 63–4, *15*, **18**, 154, **20**, 155, **36**, 161, **66–9**, 169–70

Caliche, 60
Cambering, 36, *5*, 205
Carbonaceous deposits, 57–8
Carbonates, 59–61
Chalk, 60, **47**, 164
Chamosite, 60
Chemical deposits, 47, 55–6
Chert, 61, **64**, 168–9
Chilled margin, **127**, 194, *50*
Clarain, 58
Clastic sediments, 47–8
Clasts, 48
Clay, 48, 53, **32**, 158
— ironstone, 60
— with Flints, 35, 51
Cleavage, *3*, 30, 41–3, *7*, **37**, 181
— axial plane, 42, *7*, 69
— bedding relationship, 41–2, *7*, **78**, 173–4
— fracture, 69, **81**, 171–2
— post folding, **74**, 171
— slaty, 69, **73**, 171
Coal, 48, *12*, 57–8
Coal Measures, 48, *12*, **57–60**, 167–8
Coccoliths, 60
Collapse breccia, **55**, 167
Columnar jointing, 73, **118**, 190–2, *48*
Compass/clinometer, 21–3, 208
Concretions, 53, 61, **61**, 168, **62**, 169
Cone-in-cone, 61, 169, **62**
Cone sheet, 78, **131**, 196, *51*
Conformable strata, **52**, 166
Conglomerate, 48–9, 50, **1**, 149, **5**, 151

Contact, **127**, 194, *50*, **132**, 196, **138**, 198
Coquina, **46**, 164
Corals, **48**, 164
Country rock, 76, 145
Cross cutting relationships, 74
Cross-section, *56*, 204
Cryoturbation, **14**, 152
Current bedding, 52, **21**, 155
Cyclothem, 48, *12*, 167

Deformation, pre-lithification, 53–4
Dendritic markings, 148, **152**, 202–3
Density currents, 55
Derived fossils, 62, 66
Diachronous, 65, *16*
Diapirs, 54, **42**, 162–3
Diatomaceous earth, 59
Differentiation, 79–80
Diffusion, 80, **135**, 197, **138**, 198
Diorite, **138**, 198
Dip, 21, *1*
— apparent, 23, *2*
— fault, 70
— slip fault, 71
— traverse, 26
Disconformity, 65, *16*
Discordant intrusion, 78
Dolomite, 59–60
Drift deposits, mapping of, 34–6
Drift edition, 27
Dropstone, 154
Dyke, *20*, 78, 80, **112**, 189, *47*, **128–31**, 195–6
— multiple, *20*, 78
— ring, *20*, 78
Dune bedding, **19**, 155
Durain, 58

Erosion surface, 52, **1**, 149, **18**, 154
Erratic, 35, 50
Evaporites, 56–7
Exposures between, 25–6
— critical, 16
— reading, 16
— systematic examination of, 23–4
Extrusive rocks, 74–6

Fault, *3*, 30, 45, 70–2, 19, 146, **72**, 170–1, *27*, **76**, 172, *29*, **86–8**, 178–9, *34*, **90**, 180
— breccia, 70
— conjugate, **96**, 183, *39*
— dextral, 72, **97**, 183, *40*
— drag, **86**, 178, **90**, 180
— grooves, 70
— mapping of, 38–9
— normal, 70, *19*
— oblique, 72
— plane, 70, **84**, 177–8, *34*
— reverse, 71, *19*
— sinistral, 72, **97**, 183, *40*
— tear, 71, *19*, **97**, 183, *40*
— transcurrent, 71
— wrench, 71
Feather fracture, **105**, 186–7, *45*
Feature, *3*, 30, 32–4, *4*, 40
Field equipment suppliers, 208–9
— identification, 19–20
— map, **156**, 203–4, *56*
— notebook, 17, 29–31
— sketching, 17–19
— work, care and safety, 13
— — code for, 13
— — equipment for, 12–14
— — localities for, 11–12
— — planning of, 24–5
Flake conglomerate, 64, 169
Flint, 61, **63**, 168
Flowfolds, **122**, 193
Flute casts, **36**, 161
Foliation, *3*, 30, 41, **139**, 198–9
Fold, *3*, 30, 41–3, 66–70, *17*, *18*, 146
— axial plane of, *3*, 30, 41, 66–7, *17*, **74**, 170, **141**, 199
— axial trace, *3*, 30
— conjugate, **77**, 172–3, *30*
— downward facing, 43, *8*, 171
— hinge, 41, *7*
— inverted, **74**, 171–2, *28*
— isoclinal, 68–9, *18*, **83**, 176–7, *33*, **142**, 199, *53*
— neutral, 68, *17*
— ptygmatic, **102**, 185–6, *41*, **122**, 193
— recumbent, 68, *17*

— refolded, **142**, 199
— sideways facing, 43
— upwards facing, 43, *8*
Footprints, **25**, 157
Fossils, 48, *12*, 58–9, 61–4
Framework of rock, 48
Fusain, 58

Gabbro, **136**, 197
Ganister, 58
Gash breccia, **3**, 150
Geode, 61
Geological hammer, 12–3, 208
Geological mapping, 27–46
— symbols, *3*, 30
— Survey, publications of, 205–6
— Societies, publications of, 206–8
Glacial deposits, *3*, 30, 49–51
— striations, *3*, 30, **11**, 152
Gneiss, 147, **144**, 199, **148–51**, 201–2
Gouge, 70
Graben, 70
Graded beds, 55, **35**, 160
Granite, **127**, 194, *50*, **135**, 197, **148–51**, 201–2
— intrusion, 24
Granophyre, **137**, 197
Green-schist, 147
Greisen, **135**, 197
Growth fibres, 70, **84**, 177
Gull, 36, *5*
Gypsum, *166*, **54**, 167

Handlens, 13, 208
Hard-rock geologist, 31
— mapping of, 39–46
Head, *3*, 30, 35, 51, **14**, 152–3, **16**, 154, 205
Hornfels, 145, **125**, 194, **132**, 196–7
Hyaloclastite, 75, **119**, 192

Igneous relationships, 80
— rocks, 74–80
Ignimbrite, 75
Imbricate structure, *6*, 39
Incompetent layer, 166
Information, sources of, 205–8
Interference patterns, **144**, 199
Intraformational clast, **43**, 163
Intrusive rocks, 74, 76–80
Iron carbonates, 60
Ironstone, **49**, 165, **59**, 168

Joint, *3*, 30, 44–5, *10–1*, 72–3, 148, **103**, 186, **105**, 186–7, *45*, 190–2, *48*, **114–8**, **121**, 192, **128**, 194

Laccolith, *20*, 77–8
Landslipping, 26, *3*, 30, *5*, 37, 148, **34**, 159–60, 205
Land surface, **115**, 190–1
Laterite, 51, **116**, 190–1
Lava, 74–6, **114–8**, **190–2**
Layered intrusion, 79, **134**, 197
Liesegang rings, 148, **33**, 158–9, *24*
Limestone, 59–61
— bioclastic, 59
— concretionary, **51**, 166
— nodular, **45**, 163
— oolitic, 59
— reef, 60, *14*, **44**, 163
Linear structure, 21, 23, *1*, *3*, 30
Lithomarge, 190
Lit-par-lit, **149**, 202

Magma, 78–80, 145–7
Marble, 145–6
Matrix of a rock, 48–52
Metamorphic aureole, *20*, 77
— grade, 146–7
— rocks, 145–7
Metamorphism contact, *3*, 30, 79–80, 145, **125–6**, 194
— dynamic, 145
— regional, 145–7
— thermal, 145
Migmatite, 147, **148–50**, 201–2
Mineral infilling, 44–5, 70, 73
Monocline, 68, *18*
Moraine, **17**, 154
Mudcracks, **30–1**, 158
Mudstone, 48, 53
Museums, 207–8
Mylonite, 145

Nappe, 43–4, *9*
National grid, 17
Neptunean dyke, 54, **41**, 162
Nonconformity, 65, *16*
Nué ardente, 74

Observations, recording of, 29–31, *3*
Ophiolite suite, 75
Organic deposits, 47, 57–9
Overturned beds, **79**, 174

Peat, 58
Pebbles aligned, **80**, 174
Pegmatite, 79
Pelite, 40, 147
Percussion fracture, **105**, 187
Periglacial, 35, 51
Permafrost, 51
Phenocryst, 78, **133**, 197
Phosphatic deposits, 58–9, 66
— nodules, **9**, 151, **56**, 167
Photography, 18, 209–10
Phyllite, 146, **127**, 194, *50*, **139**, 198, *52*, **141**, 199
Pillow lava, 75, **119** **20**, 192–3, *49*
Pipe, **24**, 156, **47**, 164
Pitch, 21, 23, *1*
Pitchstone, 75, **122**, 193
Plunge, 21, 23, *1*, 68, *17*, **144**, 199–200, *54*
Pluton, 77–9, *20*
Porcellanite, **125**, 194
Porphyritic texture, 78, **133**, 197
Porphyroblast, **147**, 201
Precipitation, 55, **45**, 163
Psammite, 40, 147, **142**, 199
Pumice, 76
Pyroclastic rocks, 74, 76

Quartzite, 52, 145–6, **21**, 155

Radiolarian ooze, 59
Rain pits, **25**, 157
Raised beach, **10**, 152, *44*
Rank of coal, 57
Recrystallization, 146
Reduction patches, **22**, 155
Reef, 60, *14*, **44**, 163
Regolith, **14**, 152
Replacement, 56
Report, writing of, 45–6
Residual deposits, 51
Rhythmic banding, **134**, 197
Rift valley, 70
Ripple-drift bedding, **26**, 157
— marks, **23**, 156, **40**, 162
Roche moutonnée, *3*, 30
Rose diagram, 44, *10*, 45, *13*, 56
Rudaceous rocks, 48–9

Salines, 56
Salt dome, 57, 163
Sandstone, 48, 51–3
Scarp, 32–4, **104**, 186
Schist, 145–7, **140**, 199, **142**, 199, **145**, 200, **147**, 201
Schistocity, 41, **139**, 198, *52*
Seat Earth, 48, 58, *12*, **60**, 167–8
Sedimentary rocks, 47–66
Sekbha, 166
Septarian nodule, 61, **65**, 169
Shale, 53, **28–9**, 157–8
— pyritized and silicified, **101**, 185
Shear, 41
— joint, 72
Siliceous organisms, 59
Sill, *20*, 77–8, 80, **85**, 178, **123**–7, 193–4
Siltstone, 48, 52
Slate, 53
Slickensides, 70, **84**, 177
Slumping, 53–5, **37–9**, 161
Soft-rock geologist, 31–9
Soil creep, 36, 148, **153**, 203
Solid edition, 27
Solid with Drift edition, 27
Solifluction deposits, 51, **13**, 152
Solution, 57, **47**, 164
Sorting, 52
Spheroidal weathering, 148, 190, **117**, 192
Spilite, 75
Stoping, 79
Stoss, 157

Strata horizontal, *3*, 30
— inclined, *3*, 30
— vertical, *3*, 30, **75**, 172
Stratigraphical Table, 9
Strike, 21, *1*, 22, *2*
— fault, 70
— slip fault, 71
— traverse, 26
Structural terrace, 68, *18*
Structures, bottom, 55
— geological, 66–70
— of secondary origin, 61
— small scale, 40–2, *7*, 68–9, **82**, 176, *32*, 205
— superficial, 36
Stylolites, 61, **50**, 165–6, *26*
Submerged forest, 58
Symbols for geological maps, *3*, 30
Syncline, **6**, 151, **72**, 170–1, *27*, **76**, 172, *29*, **140**, 199
Synform, *3*, 30, 43

Tension gashes, 72, **96**, 183, **100**, 184–5, *41*
— joint, 72
Terminal curvature, 148
Terrace gravels, 25
Terra rosa, 51
Thrust, *3*, 30, *6*, 39, **83**, 176–7, *33*, **91–3**, 181, *37*, **94–5**, 182
— fault, 70, *19*, 72
Tillite, 50
Trace fossil, 63–4, *15*, **21**, 155, **70–1**, 170
Trail, 63–4, *15*, **69**, 170
Travertine, 60
Tufa, 60
Tuff, **106–7**, 187–8, *46*, **109**, 188
— dyke, **108**, 188
Turbidite, 54–6, *13*, **34–41**, 160–2, *25*, **43**, 163, **67**, 169, **74**, 171
— metamorphosed, **146**, 200–1

Unconformity, 23–4, 64–6, *16*, **4–9**, 150–1, **18**, 154

Valley bulge, 36–7, *5*
Varved clay, **15**, 135
Vein, 44–5, 73–4, **98–100**, 184–5, *41–2*, **101–2**, 185–6, *42–3*, **139**, 198, *52*, **143**, 199
Vertical aerial photographs, 28, 40
Vitrain, 58
Volcano, 74–6
Volcanic ash, 76
— bomb, 76
— neck, 75, **104**, 186, *44*, **110**, **112**, 189, *47*, **113**, 190
Volcani-clastic sediments, 76
Vug, 73, **89**, 179–80, *35*

Way up evidence, 42, 62–3
Weathering of rocks, 147–8
Welded tuff, 75, **106–7**, 187–8, *46*

Xenolith, 77, *20*, 79, **113**, 190, **133**, 197, **137**, 197

Younging of beds, 42–3, *8*

MINERALS AND ROCKS IN COLOUR